WORDLY WISE

3000

Book **1**

Kenneth Hodkinson
Sandra Adams

eps

Educators Publishing Service, Inc.
Cambridge and Toronto

Cover design by Hugh Price

August 1998 Printing

Lesson 1

Word List *Study the definitions of the words below; then do the exercises for the lesson.*

benefit

v. To help or be helpful to; to be useful to.
[That preschool program *benefits* young children.]
n. 1. Something that is useful or helpful, that does good, sometimes as part of a job contract.
[One of the *benefits* of my exercise program is that I sleep better.]
2. An event held to raise money for a cause.
[The library's *benefit* raised enough money for a new children's room.]

complete

adj. 1. Having no missing parts; whole.
[She bought a *complete* set of woodworking tools at a yard sale.]
2. Finished.
[The new wing on the high school is now *complete*.]
v. To finish.
[Schubert did not *complete* his eighth symphony, so it's nicknamed "The Unfinished."]

develop

v. 1. To go through a process of growth.
[Running regularly *develops* strong leg muscles.]
2. To bring or come into being.
[The day after I brushed against the poison ivy, a rash *developed* on my leg.]
3. To apply chemicals to photographic film to bring out the picture.
[I want to learn to *develop* my own pictures.]

dismay

v. To cause feelings of fear, worry, or surprise.
[A large crack in the ceiling of our newly painted kitchen *dismayed* my parents.]
n. A sudden loss of courage because of fear or worry.
[Just after we began hiking, we were filled with *dismay* when we heard the rumble of a rockslide.]

ease

n. A state of being comfortable—without worry, pain, or trouble.
[Since I took a course in public speaking, I feel much more at *ease* when I give a speech.]
v. To make less worried, pained, or troubled.
[It *eased* my mind to hear you were safe.]

hail

n. Small lumps of frozen rain.
[The *hail* bouncing off the metal roof of the garage made a terrible racket.]
v. 1. To fall as frozen rain.
[My father's corn plants suffered a lot of damage when it *hailed* yesterday.]
2. To greet or welcome, usually with admiration.
[The band played *"Hail* to the Chief" as the president came in.]

lack

v. To be without.
[He never sees the funny side of things because he *lacks* a sense of humor.]
n. A shortage.
[A *lack* of money to pay the staff forced our library to close on weekends.]

master   *adj.* Chief; main.
[Throw the *master* switch to turn on the power.]
v. To become skilled at.
[My mother *mastered* the new computer program in just a few weeks.]

patriot   *n.* One who loves, supports, and is loyal to his or her country.
[Giuseppe Garibaldi was an Italian *patriot* who fought tirelessly to unite his country.]
patriotic   *adj.*   Having or showing love of one's country.
["America the Beautiful" is a *patriotic* song that was written by Katherine Lee Bates.]
patriotism   *n.* Love of one's country.
[Some people show their *patriotism* by proudly flying their country's flag.]

project   *n.* ('pro ject) A plan or idea for doing something.
[My science *project* is going to show what acid rain does to plants.]
v. (pro'ject) 1. To stick out.
[Nails are still *projecting* out of the new floor, so be careful where you walk.]
2. To cause an image to be shown on a screen.
[This machine *projects* color slides but not movies.]

recommend   *v.* 1. To make a statement of praise.
[I loved the *Secret Garden* and I highly *recommend* it.]
2. To give advice; to suggest.
[Dentists usually *recommend* that you have a checkup twice a year.]

remark   *v.* To say; to make a comment.
[My grandmother *remarked* on how well I looked.]
n. Something said; a comment.
[When no one else could think of anything to say, I made a *remark* about how badly we needed rain.]
remarkable   *adj.* Deserving of being noticed; unusual.
[For such a young child, he had *remarkable* strength.]

represent   *v.* 1. To stand for or in place of.
[Three dots *represent* the letter "S" in the Morse code.]
2. To act in place of.
[Each state in the U.S. elects two senators to *represent* it in Congress.]

sufficient   *adj.* Enough to fill a need.
[Ten lessons on the oboe were *sufficient* to earn me a place in the school band.]

utter   *v.* To make sounds with the voice; to speak.
[Please don't *utter* another word.]

1A Finding Meanings

Choose two phrases to form a sentence that correctly uses a word from Word List 1. Write each sentence in the space provided.

1. (a) a useful aid.　　　　　　　　(c) Dismay is
   (b) Hail is　　　　　　　　　　　(d) frozen rain.

_____

2. (a) A remarkable plan is　　　　　(c) one that will probably fail.
   (b) the main one.　　　　　　　　(d) A master plan is

_____

3. (a) a place to relax.　　　　　　　(c) A benefit is
   (b) an event that raises money.　　(d) A patriot is

_____

4. (a) A complete picture is one that is　　(c) very unusual.
   (b) A remarkable picture is one that is　(d) not easy to see.

_____

5. (a) to bring it to an end.　　　　　(c) to make it grow.
   (b) To develop something is　　　　(d) To ease something is

_____

6. (a) to control it.　　　　　　　　(c) To utter something is
   (b) To complete something is　　　(d) to say it.

_____

7. (a) stand in for him or her.　　　　(c) To represent someone is to
   (b) invite him or her.　　　　　　(d) To recommend someone is to

_____

8. (a) To lack food　　　　　　　　(c) is to have more than enough.
   (b) To have sufficient food　　　　(d) is to have enough.

_____

9. (a) to show it on a screen.　　　　(c) To recommend a picture is
   (b) to change it slightly.　　　　　(d) To project a picture is

_____

1B Just the Right Word

Improve each of the following sentences by crossing out the italicized phrase and replacing it with a word (or a form of the word) from Word List 1.

1. I sensed a *total absence* of enthusiasm when I suggested that we climb Mount Monadnock.

2. Martha Graham *brought into being* a new style of dance in America.

3. The bookshelf *sticks out* too far into the room and has to be made narrower.

4. I took a hot bath to help *to take away the pain in* my aching muscles.

5. Olga Ramirez expects her novel to be *at a point where no further work is necessary* by the end of the week.

6. My uncle *became very skilled at* speaking French after spending a year in France.

7. In English the letter "c" *stands in place of* two different sounds.

8. Young children *are helped* a great deal from being read to every day.

9. The article ended with a reminder that there is more to showing *love of one's country* than flying your country's flag.

10. The news that the last train had just left *worried and distressed* us.

11. The track coach *gave me the suggestion* that I warm up before starting my run.

1C Applying Meanings

Circle the letter of each correct answer to the questions below. A question may have more than one correct answer.

1. Which of the following might fill someone with *dismay?*
   - (a) losing ten dollars
   - (b) finding ten dollars
   - (c) finding a staple in a tuna sandwich
   - (d) finding celery in a tuna sandwich

2. Which of the following might put someone at *ease?*
   - (a) a friendly smile
   - (b) a "Keep Out" sign
   - (c) a warm welcome
   - (d) a promise to help

3. Which of the following might be *hailed* by people?
   (a) a train crash
   (b) a cure for a disease
   (c) a popular president
   (d) rain after a long dry spell

4. Which of the following is a *complete* sentence and needs a period?
   (a) I'm cold
   (b) Let's go
   (c) The bus for Toledo
   (d) My hockey puck

5. A rich person could *lack* which of the following?
   (a) money
   (b) freedom
   (c) time
   (d) good health

6. Which of the following could mean a person is *patriotic*?
   (a) making money
   (b) having a hobby
   (c) voting in elections
   (d) serving one's country

7. Which of the following is a *remark*?
   (a) You look tired.
   (b) 2 + 2 = 4
   (c) What on earth are you doing?
   (d) A B C D

8. Which of the following *represent* other people?
   (a) state senators
   (b) taxi drivers
   (c) storekeepers
   (d) lawyers

1D Completing the Thought

Read each sentence below and fill in the blank with the correct word (or a form of the word) from the word list.

1. Jennifer can fly for half price because she works for an airline. Half-price travel is one of her _____.

2. Nebraska plans to spend six million dollars building a new bridge over the Platte River. The new bridge is a state _____.

3. Yehudi Menuhin was one of the greatest violin players who ever lived. As a child, he was unusually talented, and _____ the violin at a very early age.

4. Leslie answered all the questions on the test and still had time to check her answers. She _____ the test with time to spare.

5. The Changs decided to try the Golden Grill because their friends told them that the food there was delicious. They went there because their friends _____ it.

benefit
complete
hail
master
patriot
project
recommend
remark
sufficient
utter

6. The white-haired man sitting next to her told Marie that she reminded him of his favorite granddaughter. This _____ made Marie happy.

7. Tony's gas level was low when he got on the expressway. He was afraid he would not have _____ gas to get home.

8. Jamile remained silent when she was asked where her friend was staying. She did not _____ a sound.

9. Alexander Hamilton and Thomas Jefferson disagreed on many things, but both had the best interests of the United States at heart. They were both _____.

10. The afternoon was dark and cold; the rain was beginning to freeze. Soon we could hear the plink-plink of the _____.

1E Narrative   *Read the narrative below; then complete the exercise that follows.*

SEQUOYA'S GIFT

Sequoya was a **remarkable** man—a silversmith, painter, and soldier who is famous because he is the only person in history known to have invented a complete alphabet.

Sequoya was a member of the Cherokee nation, the son of a Native American mother and a British father. A **patriotic** person, he was **dismayed** that white people were taking over more and more of the Cherokee lands.

There was no easy way for Cherokees to be in touch with each other because they **lacked** a written language. Words spoken in Cherokee were lost as soon as they were **uttered.** Sequoya believed that the Cherokee people would **benefit** greatly if they had a written language and could read and write. Then newspapers could spread the word of what was happening to people, and books could record their history. He made up his mind that he would try to **develop** a written language for his people.

The **project,** which he began in 1809, took twelve years to **complete.** He and his daughter worked together. She carefully sounded out each syllable, and Sequoya **represented** it with a letter that he chose from the English, Greek, and Hebrew alphabets. Eighty-six letters were **sufficient** to cover all the sounds of the Cherokee language.

Sequoya used this new written language in a message he sent to the leaders of the Cherokee nation. The leaders were impressed with how simple the system was, and they **recommended** that the new written language be taught to everyone who wanted to learn to read and write. People liked it because it could be learned quickly and with ease, and those who **mastered** it went on to teach others. The Cherokees set up schools to teach Sequoya's alphabet and began to publish books and newspapers in their new language. The first Native American newspaper, the *Cherokee Phoenix*, was published on February 21, 1828. It was followed by a flood of other newspapers and books.

In his later years, Sequoya travelled throughout North America studying other Native American languages. Everywhere he went he was **hailed** for his invention, which played such an important part in uniting the Cherokee people. He died in 1843. His memory is honored in California's giant sequoia trees, and its beautiful Sequoia National Park.

Answer each of the following questions in a sentence. If a question does not contain a vocabulary word, use a vocabulary word in your answer. Use each word only once. Questions and answers will then contain all fifteen words (or forms of the words) from this lesson's word list.

1. How can we tell that Sequoya was **patriotic**?

   _____

2. What is the meaning of **utter** as used in the narrative?

   _____

3. Why weren't any books written in Cherokee before 1821?

   _____

4. How did Sequoya feel about what the white settlers were doing?

   _____

5. What is the meaning of **develop** as it is used in the narrative?

   _____

6. How did Sequoya use the English, Greek and Hebrew alphabets?

   _____

7. Our alphabet has twenty-six letters. Why wasn't that number **sufficient** for the Cherokee alphabet?

   _____

8. How long did Sequoya's work take?

   _____

9. Did Sequoya work on his **project** alone or did he have help?

_____

10. Why was the new language popular with the people?

_____

11. How can we tell that the Cherokee leaders liked the new system?

_____

12. What is the meaning of **hailed** as it is used in the narrative?

_____

13. How did the Cherokees help each other learn the new language?

_____

14. What was **remarkable** about Sequoya?

_____

15. How does a written language **benefit** friends living far apart?

_____

WORDLY WISE

The Latin *bene* means "good" or "well" and forms a root of the word **benefit**. A *benefit* is something that is good for a person. Other words formed from this root include *benevolent,* which means "having a wish to do good" and *beneficial,* which means "doing good; being of help."

Some people, the Germans, for example, think of their country as a father and call it the fatherland; in fact, the word **patriot** comes from the Latin *pater,* which means "father." People of other countries, including Americans, think of their country not as the fatherland but as the motherland. If English had used the Latin word for mother, which is *mater,* instead of the word for father, what would we call a person with a deep love of country? *

In addition to its meaning as a verb, **utter** is also an adjective and means "total" or "absolute." [When the cellar door slammed shut behind us, we were left in *utter* darkness.]; [I felt like an *utter* fool when the bike I had reported stolen was found just where I had left it.]

*A matriot.

Lesson 2

Word List

Study the definitions of the words below; then do the exercises for the lesson.

affect
    v. 1. To bring about a change in.
[Do you think changing schools will *affect* my grades?]
2. To pretend to be or to have.
[The reporter *affected* an interest in buying a used car in order to get the salesperson to talk to her.]

calculate
    v. 1. To find the answer by using arithmetic.
[I gave my sister the check so she could *calculate* her share of the bill.]
2. To figure out by reasoning.
[You'd better *calculate* the risks carefully before going on a long trip with that old car.]

climate
    n. The average weather conditions of an area.
[Florida's warm *climate* is perfect for growing oranges.]

column
    n. 1. A row of figures or words running down a printed page; anything arranged like that.
[Do all the problems in the first *column* on page 30.]
2. A tall, usually stone support that holds up something.
[Forty-six marble *columns* support the roof of the Parthenon in Athens.]
3. A regular newspaper or magazine article usually written by the same person.
[My mother writes a weekly sports *column* for the *News-Tribune*.]

decay
    v. To rot.
[Leaves left on the ground will *decay* over the winter.]
    n. A breaking down or rotting.
[Dentists say tooth *decay* can be prevented by regular brushing and flossing.]

exceed
    v. 1. To be more than.
[The final score of Monday's game *exceeded* our best hopes.]
2. To go beyond what is allowed.
[The officer who stopped me told me never to *exceed* the speed limit again.]
    excess *n.* More than enough; an extra amount.
[Use what you need, and save the *excess*.]
    excessive *adj.* Too much or too great.
[Last winter my parents paid an *excessive* amount for heating oil.]

forbid
    v. To order not to do something.
[A state law *forbids* smoking in hospitals.]
    forbidden *adj.* Not allowed.
[Eating in class is *forbidden*.]

grove
    n. A group of trees growing together with open space between them.
[The children walked hand in hand through the *grove* of lemon trees.]

limb   *n.* 1. An arm, leg, or wing.
                 [Bats use their webbed front and back *limbs* to fly.]
                 2. A large tree branch.
                 [The owl was perched on the top *limb* of the tree.]

mammoth   *adj.* Very large; huge.
                 [The *mammoth* Seattle Skydome holds over fifty thousand people.]

mature   *v.* To become fully grown or developed.
                 [Rabbits *mature* in about six months and are then able to bear young.]
                 adj. Fully grown or developed; adult.
                 [My brother looks very *mature* for only eleven.]

permit   *v.* (per ′mit) To allow.
                 [Some towns *permit* overnight parking downtown.]

                 n. (′per mit) A written notice that allows a person to do something.
                 [You need a *permit* to go fishing in that lake.]

resist   *v.* 1. To refuse to give in to; to withstand.
                 [Some kinds of corn *resist* disease better than others.]
                 2. To work or fight against.
                 [The people tried for years to *resist* the party's leader.]

scorch   *v.* To burn slightly.
                 [If you press a shirt with an iron that is too hot, you might *scorch* the cloth.]
                 scorching *adj.* Very hot.
                 [On such a *scorching* July day, the only thing I wanted after work was a swim in the ocean.]

tower   *v.* To stand above or higher than what is around it.
                 [The Statue of Liberty *towers* above New York Harbor.]
                 towering *adj.* Very high; tall.
                 [Looking up at the *towering* skyscrapers gave me a stiff neck.]

2A Finding Meanings

Choose two phrases to form a sentence that correctly uses a word from Word List 2. Write each sentence in the space provided.

1. (a) keep people out of a building.   (c) A column is used to
   (b) support part of a building.   (d) A permit is used to

_____

2. (a) A maple grove is   (c) A maple limb is
   (b) what is left after it is cut down.   (d) a large branch.

_____

3. (a) A mammoth parade is   (c) one held once a year.
   (b) A forbidden parade is   (d) one that is very large.

_____

4. (a) To scorch something is to   (c) look closely into it.
    (b) To permit something is to   (d) allow it.

---

5. (a) A climate is   (c) a group of paintings.
    (b) a group of trees.   (d) A grove is

---

6. (a) To calculate something is to   (c) To affect something is to
    (b) figure it out by reasoning.   (d) be against it.

---

7. (a) If something towers,   (c) it is starting to grow.
    (b) If something decays,   (d) it stands above what is around it.

---

8. (a) to go beyond it.   (c) To exceed something is
    (b) To forbid something is   (d) to go back to it.

---

9. (a) To resist something is   (c) to cause a change in it.
    (b) To affect something is   (d) to forget about it.

---

10. (a) an extra amount.   (c) a shortage.
    (b) A climate is   (d) An excess is

2B Just the Right Word

Improve each of the following sentences by crossing out the italicized phrase and replacing it with a word (or a form of the word) from Word List 2.

1. Pat's *regular newspaper article* on gardening is very popular with readers.

2. Unfortunately, the cost of those sneakers *is more than* what I've saved so far.

3. I tried to *figure out* how much gas we would use on our trip to Nevada.

4. You'll have to *pretend to have* a Southern accent if you want to play Atticus in *To Kill a Mockingbird*.

5. Young people *develop into adults* much earlier than they used to.

6. Arizona's *usual weather* is very dry.

7. My parents *do not allow* television during the week.

8. Even though I'm dieting, I find it hard to *avoid giving in to my wish for* fried foods.

9. If you apply heat to a compost pile it speeds up the *process of the breaking down* of vegetable matter.

10. It was such a(n) *extremely hot* sun that the plants on our front steps were all drooping.

2C Applying Meanings

Circle the letter of each correct answer to the questions below. A question may have more than one correct answer.

1. Which of the following could be thought of as *towering*?
   (a) an eight-foot person
   (b) an eight-foot tree
   (c) a 100-foot flagpole
   (d) a 500-foot hill

2. For which of the following might you need a *permit*?
   (a) hunting a deer
   (b) setting lobster traps
   (c) keeping a dog
   (d) owning a goldfish

3. Which of the following help(s) the body to *resist* disease?
   (a) greasy food
   (b) exercise
   (c) germs
   (d) smoking

4. Which of the following *decay(s)*?
   (a) snow and ice
   (b) metal posts
   (c) fallen trees
   (d) cut grass

5. Which of the following are *forbidden*?
   (a) stealing
   (b) cheating
   (c) complaining
   (d) speeding

6. Which of the following can be *scorched*?
   (a) a person's skin
   (b) a new shirt
   (c) a clever idea
   (d) a pool of water

7. In which of the following might you see a *grove* of trees?
   - (a) a large park
   - (b) a large field
   - (c) a parking lot
   - (d) a tall building

8. Which of the following is a *limb*?
   - (a) a bird's wing
   - (b) a bird's leg
   - (c) a tree branch
   - (d) a tree root

2D Completing the Thought

Read each sentence below and fill in the blank with the correct word (or a form of the word) from the word list.

column
decay
exceed
forbid
mammoth
mature
permit
resist
scorch
tower

1. Marguerita wanted to go to the rock concert, but she didn't want to pay seventy-five dollars for a ticket! She thought that the price was _____.

2. Sarah wanted to feed her cats scraps from the dinner table, but she couldn't. Feeding the cats from the table was _____.

3. The last time Jonathan went to the dentist he didn't need any fillings. There was no sign of tooth _____.

4. This was the first year that Mr. Rodriguez got a good crop of apples from the tree that he planted five years ago. A tree doesn't produce fruit until it is _____.

5. The school librarian said that we could talk as long as we kept our voices down. The librarian _____ quiet talking.

6. Many Americans objected to the war in Vietnam and they would not fight in it. They _____ the draft.

7. José checked the numbers running down the left side of the page and compared them to those running down the right side. The numbers on the page were in two _____.

8. The winning pumpkin at the county fair weighed over 500 pounds. It was _____!

9. An unpleasant smell told Sally that the wet socks she had hung on a stick to dry were too close to the campfire. When she examined them, she saw that the socks were _____.

10. When I went up in the elevator with the basketball team's star forward I felt tiny! Even though I'm 5'10" he _____ over me.

2E Narrative   *Read the narrative below, then complete the exercise that follows.*

CALIFORNIA'S FOREST GIANTS

Along the coast of northern California grow huge, **towering** trees whose trunks look like the **columns** of a great Greek temple. These are redwood trees—the tallest of all trees—so tall in fact, that they can reach 385 feet. Their trunks can grow straight up for 150 feet before the first **limbs** branch out. One redwood, called the Rockefeller Tree, is as tall as a thirty-five-story skyscraper!

Redwoods are so special that in some parts of California state laws **forbid** people to cut them down. In other parts of the state, where logging is **permitted**, redwood is sold for outside building and outdoor furniture because it does not **decay** as quickly as other kinds of wood.

Another giant California tree is the sequoia, a tree that is slightly shorter than a redwood. Sequoias prefer the colder, drier **climate** found farther inland on the slopes of the Sierra Nevada. They have thicker trunks and contain more wood than redwoods. In fact, it has been **calculated** that a full-grown sequoia contains enough wood to build thirty houses. The **mammoth** General Grant sequoia is almost a hundred feet around. It would take twenty people with arms stretched out to join hands around it! Cutting down any sequoia is not allowed.

Redwoods and sequoias are among the oldest living things: the age of some of them **exceeds** three thousand years. One of the reasons they live so long is that when they are **mature**, their bark is more than a foot thick. Forest fires that destroy other trees may **scorch** their outside bark, but do not **affect** them. The thick bark also helps them to **resist** diseases that kill other trees.

Yosemite National Park and Sequoia National Park, both in eastern California, are the best places to see sequoias. The best place to see redwoods is in Redwood National Park, in northwest California. In addition to its **groves** of redwoods, this park also contains forty miles of unspoiled Pacific coastline. These parks are among the most popular tourist attractions in the country.

Answer each of the following questions in a sentence. If a question does not contain a vocabulary word, use a vocabulary word in your answer. Use each word only once. Questions and answers will then contain all fifteen words (or forms of the words) from this lesson's word list.

1. What happens to sequoias and redwoods in a forest fire?

   _____

2. Where can you find **groves** of redwoods?

   _____

3. If you lived in California, could you cut down a redwood tree?

   _____

4. How far from the ground are the lowest branches of the redwoods?

   _____

5. What do the trunks of redwoods look like?

   _____

6. How old are the oldest sequoia and redwood trees?

   _____

7. Why is **towering** a good word to use to describe these trees?

   _____

8. When is their bark thickest?

   _____

9. How else does their thick bark help the trees?

   _____

10. Could you cut down a sequoia?

   _____

11. Why is redwood used for building outside furniture?

   _____

12. Why don't sequoias grow along the coast?

   _____

13. How thick is the trunk of the General Grant tree?

   _____

14. How much wood does a full-grown sequoia contain?

   _____

15. Why have redwoods and sequoias lived so long?

   _____

WORDLY WISE

An easy way to learn simple arithmetic is to set out pebbles in a row. By adding more pebbles and counting the total, or by taking some away and counting the ones that remain, one can see the results of addition and subtraction. By using rows of pebbles, one can also learn multiplication. Pebbles arranged in three rows of four can be counted one at a time to see that 3 times 4 equals 12. By separating the pebbles into equal-sized groups, one can also learn division. For example, dividing the pebbles into two equal groups and counting the pebbles in one of them shows that 12 divided by 2 equals six. The Romans long ago thought of this method of doing math. In fact, our word **calculate** comes from the Latin word *calculus,* which means—a pebble!

Tens of thousands of years ago, a giant elephant lived in Europe and North America. It was called a mammoth. It was much bigger than today's elephants; the largest ones were almost fourteen feet from the ground to the shoulder. It had huge tusks that curved downward and a thick, hairy coat. Mammoths died out long ago, but the bodies of some of them were frozen solid in the cold northern regions of Canada and Russia. They are sometimes discovered when the ice around them melts. Because of this creature's great size, its name became the adjective **mammoth,** meaning "very large; huge."

Lesson 3

Word List

Study the definitions of the words below; then do the exercises for the lesson.

approach *v.* To go closer to.
[The vet *approached* the wounded deer carefully.]
n. 1. A coming closer.
[My grandparents dread the *approach* of winter.]
2. A road or way that leads to a place.
[The *approach* to the beach was blocked by a fallen tree.]

burrow *v.* 1. To dig a hole or tunnel into or under something.
[Turtles *burrow* into soft sand to lay their eggs.]
2. To dig deeply into; to search.
[The clerk *burrowed* through the pile of papers on his desk.]
n. A hole or tunnel dug by an animal as a home or for protection.
[A mole spends most of its time in its *burrow.*]

cease *v.* To stop; to come or bring to an end.
[After several hours of thunder and lightning, the storm finally *ceased.*]

destructive *adj.* Causing harm or damage.
[Cutworms are very *destructive* garden insects.]
destruction *n.* Harm or damage.
[When Hurricane Andrew hit the Florida coast, it caused great *destruction.*]

drowsy *adj.* Tired or sleepy.
[Lying in the sun always makes my cat, Inky, *drowsy.*]

famished *adj.* Very hungry.
[Sometimes I work through my lunch hour, so by suppertime I am *famished!*]

forecast *v.* To figure out and say what will happen before it takes place.
[Our fishing guide *forecast* a good catch.]
n. A telling of what will happen.
[As soon as Carlos gets up he turns on the weather *forecast.*]

hibernate *v.* To spend the winter in a resting state.
[Bears *hibernate* because they can't find enough food in the winter.]

migrate *v.* To move from one country or region to another.
[Many Latin Americans have *migrated* to this country in search of work.]
migration *n.* The act of migrating.
[My friend Sandhya is studying Indian *migration* to the United States.]
migratory *adj.* Moving from one place or country to another, usually regularly.
[Canada geese are *migratory* birds.]

nestle *v.* 1. To settle down comfortably, as if in a nest.
["The children were *nestled* all snug in their beds. . ." is a famous line from *'Twas the Night before Christmas.*]
2. To lie in a sheltered, partly hidden place.
[The little Swiss town *nestled* at the foot of the Alps.]

17

observe   *v.* 1. To see; to notice.
[I looked up at the sky and *observed* a hawk circling slowly far above us.]
2. To comment; to remark.
[Sleepily, I *observed* that it was time we left.]
3. To mark an event or day.
[We *observed* Martin Luther King Day by closing the store.]
4. To obey.
[I try to *observe* the speed limit when I drive.]

prepare   *v.* To make or get ready.
[The scouts *prepared* for their camping trip by getting lots of freeze-dried food.]
preparation   *n.* Something done to get ready.
[Antonio and Ruth did most of the *preparation* for the cookout the night before.]

reduce   *v.* To make or become smaller or less.
[This winter, Vermont *reduced* the amount of salt it put on its roads.]
reduction   *n.* The act of reducing or the amount by which something is reduced.
[The store sold out of swimsuits after its huge price *reduction*.]

severe   *adj.* 1. Very strict or harsh.
[That's a very *severe* punishment for turning a paper in late.]
2. Hard to bear or deal with.
[A *severe* frost caused a lot of damage to central Florida's orange crop.]

venture   *v.* To dare to do, to go, or to say.
[Maria *ventured* onto the dance floor even though she didn't know how to dance.]
n. Something that involves the risk of a loss.
[Grandpa's most successful *venture* was a carpet cleaning service.]

3A Finding Meanings

Choose two phrases to form a sentence that correctly uses a word from Word List 3. Write each sentence in the space provided.

1. (a) does a lot of damage.   (c) can be easily tamed.
    (b) A migratory animal is one that (d) A destructive animal is one that

_____

2. (a) a disappearance.   (c) An approach is
    (b) A venture is   (d) a coming closer.

_____

3. (a) A famished creature   (c) moves with the changing seasons.
    (b) A migratory creature   (d) goes to sleep for the winter.

_____

4. (a) To burrow is to   (c) refuse to obey.
    (b) dig a hole or tunnel.   (d) To nestle is to

5. (a) to take no part in it.   (c) to say it will happen.
    (b) To forecast an event is   (d) To observe an event is

6. (a) To reduce is to   (c) To nestle is to
    (b) settle down comfortably.   (d) fall into a deep sleep.

7. (a) Preparation is   (c) Hibernation is
    (b) what you do to get ready.   (d) what is asked for.

8. (a) something that involves a risk.   (c) A reduction is
    (b) the addition of something.   (d) A venture is

9. (a) very thirsty.   (c) To be famished is to be
    (b) very hungry.   (d) To be drowsy is to be

10. (a) To observe something is to   (c) To cease something is to
    (b) pay no attention to it.   (d) notice it.

3B Just the Right Word

Improve each of the following sentences by crossing out the italicized phrase and replacing it with a word (or a form of the word) from Word List 3.

1. Hana was starting to feel *very sleepy* when a loud noise made her jump.

2. The rain did not *come to an end* until early the next morning.

3. Some animals *go into a long, deep sleep* because there is so little for them to eat during the winter months.

4. The cottage *lay partly hidden* in a hollow beside a grove of poplar trees.

5. All the *roads that lead* to the airport are closed because of the snowstorm.

6. The *long journey* of Canada geese from northern Canada to South America occurs each fall.

7. Even though Granny has *very bad* arthritis, she still tries to walk every day.

8. The *cutting down in size* of this week's newspaper to just four pages was due to the paper shortage.

9. Ron *dug deeply* through the papers on his desk, trying to find the letter from his father.

10. As Maria Tipo played the piano, I *closely watched* the way she used the pedal.

3C Applying Meanings

Circle the letter of each correct answer to the questions below. A question may have more than one correct answer.

1. Which of the following can people *reduce?*
   (a) their weight
   (b) their shoe size
   (c) their age
   (d) their spending

2. Which of the following would be a *severe* punishment?
   (a) a slap on the wrist
   (b) going to jail
   (c) no television for a year
   (d) being told to be quiet

3. Which of the following can a person *forecast?*
   (a) the result of a game
   (b) the weather
   (c) a past event
   (d) costs of doing business

4. Which of the following can cause *destruction?*
   (a) forest fires
   (b) floods
   (c) bombs
   (d) hurricanes

5. Which of the following could *cease?*
   (a) fighting
   (b) noises
   (c) the weather
   (d) a storm

6. Which of the following can *migrate?*
   (a) animals
   (b) birds
   (c) plants
   (d) humans

7. Which of the following could be *observed?*
   (a) a law
   (b) a birthday
   (c) a rule
   (d) a full moon

8. Which of the following can be *prepared?*
   (a) a lunch for four
   (b) a garden for planting
   (c) a book report
   (d) a full moon

3D Completing the Thought

Read each sentence below and fill in the blank with the correct word, (or a form of the word) from the word list.

1. We jumped into bed quickly when we heard footsteps on the stairs. We were sure our parents were _____.

2. It will take years for the Alaskan coastline to recover from the *Exxon Valdez* oil spill. The spill was very _____.

3. Our science teacher asked us if we knew why bats are hardly ever seen during the winter in cold climates. In winter, bats _____, she said.

4. Mrs. Columbo sat down for a minute and couldn't believe it when she opened her eyes to find that half an hour had passed. She must have been very _____.

approach
destructive
drowsy
famished
forecast
hibernate
migrate
prepare
reduce
venture

5. Because she wanted to do well on the biology test, Alice was careful to go over her notes with her older sister. Her sister helped her _____ for the test.

6. When Mrs. Bromberg said that she could not afford $2,000 for the repairs to the roof, the roofer offered to do the work for $1,500. He _____ the price by $500.

7. In December, Professor Wong said that the number of people finding work would go up in the new year. His _____ turned out to be correct.

8. Although Mr. Walpole was afraid of slipping on the icy sidewalk, he decided to walk to the corner store when he ran out of bread. He _____ out in spite of the ice.

9. Hector overslept, so he missed breakfast; then he lost his lunch box. By dinnertime, he was _____.

10. At the end of the summer, people in Mexico can suddenly see flocks of monarch butterflies in the sky. It is the monarch's annual _____.

3E Narrative   *Read the narrative below; then complete the exercise that follows.*

A LONG WINTER NAP

Summer is a good time of year for most animals. It's easy for them to keep warm, and food is plentiful. Winter is harder for them. Lakes and ponds are frozen, snow may cover the ground, and food is much harder to find. Many birds and some animals escape northern winters by **migrating** south in the fall and returning in the spring.

The woodchuck, or groundhog, as it is also called, deals with winter differently. It **hibernates**. As soon as it feels the weather turning cold, it digs a **burrow** at least five feet underground and makes a comfortable nest with leaves and grass. It spends the cold winter months **nestled** in its underground bed, and does not usually wake up until spring. It is far enough below ground so that there is no danger that it will freeze to death even during the most **severe** winter.

Since it will not eat at all during the winter, the woodchuck eats as much and as often as it can during the summer. People with gardens know how **destructive** one can be to their plants. As winter **approaches**, the woodchuck becomes so fat it can hardly move. It gets ready for its long sleep by **preparing** its nest and closing off the openings of the tunnels that lead down to it. When it starts to feel **drowsy**, it makes itself comfortable and falls into a long, deep sleep that can last up to eight months.

If you **observed** the woodchuck in this state, you might think it had died. Its breathing almost **ceases**, and its heart slows down to about four beats a minute. If you took its temperature, you would find that it had fallen to just above freezing. When the woodchuck wakes up in the spring after going without food for so many months, its weight has been **reduced** to only half of what it was in the fall. Almost all its body fat has been used up to keep it alive during its long sleep. By February or March, the **famished** animal is ready to leave its hole and go looking for its first meal.

Years ago, people who lived in the country eagerly awaited the sight of the first groundhog putting its head above ground; it was a sign that winter was over. This gave rise to a number of stories. One of them, told by German farmers who had settled in Punxsutawney, Pennsylvania, was about a groundhog they called Punxsutawney Phil. This remarkable animal could **forecast** the weather.

According to the story, Phil **ventured** from his nest every February 2. He poked his head above ground and looked around. If he saw his shadow, it meant that there would be another month and a half of winter, so he went back to sleep for another six weeks. If the weather was cloudy, and he didn't see his shadow, it meant spring would be early. This story spread around the country, and February 2 became known as Groundhog Day.

Answer each of the following questions in a sentence. If a question does not contain a vocabulary word, use a vocabulary word in your answer. Use each word only once. Questions and answers will then contain all fifteen words (or forms of the words) from this lesson's word list.

1. Why do you almost never see woodchucks in winter?

    _____

2. What **preparations** does a woodchuck make for winter?

    _____

3. How does the woodchuck's appearance change as winter **approaches**?

    _____

4. How does a woodchuck feel just before it begins its long sleep?

    _____

5. How do woodchucks keep from freezing during the winter months?

    _____

6. What might the temperature be during a **severe** winter?

    _____

7. How do we know that a woodchuck needs only a little oxygen during its winter sleep?

    _____

8. What does the woodchuck do when it gets into its **burrow**?

    _____

9. How does the woodchuck's size change over the winter?

    _____

10. What is the meaning of **observe** as it is used in the narrative?

    _____

11. Why is the woodchuck **famished** when it wakes up in early spring?

   _____

12. What was unusual about Punxsutawney Phil?

   _____

13. What is supposed to happen on Groundhog Day?

   _____

14. What do many northern birds do to escape the winter?

   _____

15. Why do gardeners think woodchucks are **destructive**?

   _____

WORDLY WISE

French, Spanish, and Italian are Latin languages. This means that many of their words come directly from the Latin that people throughout the Roman Empire spoke two thousand years ago. For example, the French word for *winter,* which is *hiver,* comes from the Latin *hibernum,* which means *winter.*

When modern science began several hundred years ago, there was a need for scientific terms, and these were usually formed from Latin, the language of scholars. The word **hibernate** was formed in this way. It means "to go into a sleeplike state during the winter," and comes from the Latin word for *winter.*

Lesson 4

Word List

Study the definitions of the words below; then do the exercises for the lesson.

active
adj. 1. Taking part; working.
[Luis has been an *active* member of the chess club for two years.]
2. Lively; quick; busy.
[Even though she is over ninety, Dr. O'Brien still has a very *active* mind.]
3. Moving a lot; moving quickly.
[Since I've been more physically *active,* I can run around the track more easily.]

astound
v. To surprise; to amaze.
[The United States *astounded* the world in 1969 by landing people on the moon.]
astounding *adj.* Very surprising.
[The news of Truman's election was *astounding* to Governor Dewey.]

attend
v. 1. To go to or be present at.
[If you are planning to *attend* the lunchroom committee meeting, please let Mr. Minh know.]
2. To pay attention to.
[The judge asked the jury to *attend* carefully to what she was going to say.]

cherish
v. 1. To cling to an idea or feeling.
[Ramona *cherished* the hope that her father would return soon.]
2. To take good care of; to love.
[I *cherish* the gold watch my grandfather gave me.]

contract
v. (con ′tract) 1. To make an agreement that has the force of law.
[We *contracted* with carpenters to repair the stairs.]
2. To get; to come to have.
[When I *contracted* chicken pox, Dr. Robey told me I had to stay away from other people.]
3. To make or become smaller.
[By 1828, Cherokee lands had *contracted* to one–tenth the size they had been a hundred years earlier.]
n. (′con tract) An agreement that has the force of law.
[Tom has just signed a *contract* with a publisher for his first book on the copper miners.]

eager
adj. Wanting very much.
[We were *eager* to take part in the science project.]
eagerly *adv.* With a great deal of enthusiasm, wanting.
[We *eagerly* awaited the arrival of our cousins, whom we hadn't seen in several months.]

expose   *v.* 1. To make known.
[In her weekly newspaper column, Molly Ivins *exposed* the plan to cut health benefits.]
2. To open to view.
[Cleaning the painting *exposed* the original colors.]
3. To leave unprotected.
[Since I had no place to keep my bike, I had to leave it outside, *exposed* to the weather.]

grace   *n.* 1. Beauty of form or movement.
[Margot Fonteyn danced with such *grace* that she was hailed as one of the world's greatest ballerinas.]
2. A short prayer said before a meal.
[They always say *grace* in her family.]
3. An extra period to do or pay something.
[The painters had three days *grace* to finish the house.]
graceful   *adj.* Having beauty of movement.
[With a *graceful* leap the cat landed on my lap.]

impose   *v.* 1. To force someone to accept or put up with.
[The new coach *imposed* strict rules about arriving late or leaving practice early.]
2. To take unfair advantage of.
[I try not to *impose* on my mother's good nature.]

modest   *adj.* 1. Not thinking too highly of oneself.
[Nadia was too *modest* to accept all the credit for her part in producing the play.]
2. Simple; not fancy or extreme.
[The Wallmans lived in the same *modest* apartment all their lives.]
modesty   *n.* The quality of being modest.
[Andrew wrote a book on *modesty,* but he made sure his name was in big print.]

parallel   *adj.* 1. Lying in the same direction and always the same distance apart.
[The two edges of a ruler are *parallel*.]
2. Similar.
[The reports of people who have climbed Mt. Everest are strikingly *parallel* in many respects.]

paralyze   *v.* 1. To stop all movement or feeling in.
[As the huge wave approached, fear *paralyzed* people walking at the water's edge and they stood there motionless.]
2. To make helpless or powerless.
[The snowstorm *paralyzed* Washington D.C. for five days.]
paralysis   *n.* Condition of being paralyzed.
[President Franklin D. Roosevelt used a wheelchair because of the *paralysis* of his legs.]

pessimist   *n.* A person who expects things to turn out badly.
[A *pessimist* carries an umbrella even though the forecast is for fine weather.]
pessimistic *adj.* Not having hope, joy, or confidence; gloomy.
[After losing her librarian's job, Ms. Merkelson was *pessimistic* about finding another library position in the same town.]

recite   *v.* To say aloud before an audience, usually from memory.
[Rozzie *recited* her favorite Emily Dickinson poem to the class.]
recital   *n.* A program of music or dance.
[I felt very nervous before my ballet *recital*.]

respond   *v.* To answer.
                     [When you want to *respond* to a question, please raise your hand.]
                     response   *n.* Something said or done in reply.
                     [Henry took a few moments to think before giving his *response* to Mr. Bartlett's
                     question.]

4A Finding Meanings

Choose two phrases to form a sentence that correctly uses a word from Word List 4. Write each sentence in the space provided.

1. (a) to love that person.
   (b) To cherish someone is

   (c) To expose someone is
   (d) to fear that person.

   _____

2. (a) A response is
   (b) an increase in size.

   (c) Paralysis is
   (d) an answer.

   _____

3. (a) that causes shock and surprise.
   (b) An astounding reply is one

   (c) An eager reply is one
   (d) that is not spoken.

   _____

4. (a) To contract is
   (b) To attend is

   (c) to make an agreement.
   (d) to be afraid.

   _____

5. (a) are not hidden from view.
   (b) Exposed beams

   (c) Parallel beams
   (d) meet at a corner.

   _____

6. (a) To attend a speech is
   (b) To recite a speech is

   (c) to make changes in it.
   (d) to be present at it.

   _____

7. (a) being ashamed of one's actions.
   (b) Eagerness is

   (c) Pessimism is
   (d) wanting something very much.

   _____

8. (a) Graceful lines are   (c) the same distance apart.
    (b) Parallel lines are   (d) curving away from each other.

---

9. (a) a loss of the ability to move.   (c) a belief that things will turn out badly.
    (b) Modesty is   (d) Paralysis is

---

10. (a) A recital is   (c) A pessimist is
    (b) a written agreement.   (d) one who is gloomy.

---

11. (a) Grace is   (c) beauty of movement.
    (b) Modesty is   (d) failing to do what is right.

4B Just the Right Word

Improve each of the following sentences by crossing out the italicized phrase and replacing it with a word (or a form of the word) from Word List 4.

1. Where the paint has peeled off the house, the wood will be *left unprotected* and unable to stand up to scorching summer heat and severe winter cold.

2. The magician promised that his next trick would *create great amazement in* us.

3. Eleanor Roosevelt's *lack of feelings of self-importance* impressed all who knew her.

4. Heavy snow *stopped the movement of* traffic in Denver for two days.

5. The librarian gave me one week's *extra time* to pay the fine.

6. Only about half of the members of the gardening club are *taking part in what is going on.*

7. Unfortunately, my roomate is a *person who usually expects things to turn out badly,* so he's not a very cheerful person to live with.

8. I was afraid I was *forcing myself on them* when I stayed an extra week at the Mendelssohns.

9. The pupil of the eye *becomes smaller* in bright light.

10. Did you *give your attention* to the dinner invitation from Aunt Helen?

4C Applying Meanings

Circle the letter of each correct answer to the questions below. A question may have more than one correct answer.

1. Which of the following could a person *attend?*
    (a) a patient   (c) a meeting
    (b) a concert   (d) a request

2. Which of the following can be *contracted?*
    (a) an illness   (c) muscles
    (b) the pupils of the eyes   (d) a habit

3. Which of the following requires a person to be *active?*
    (a) playing hockey   (c) walking the dog
    (b) washing windows   (d) watching television

4. Which of the following can be *paralyzed?*
    (a) a person's lower limbs   (c) a person's hair
    (b) a person's body   (d) a person's clothes

5. Which of the following might a *modest* person say?
    (a) "I had very little to do with it." (c) "You deserve all the credit."
    (b) "Please don't bother to thank me." (d) "I am the greatest!"

6. Which of the following might a *pessimistic* person say?
    (a) "Everything will be all right."   (c) "We're bound to lose."
    (b) "It's no use trying."   (d) "Next time we'll try harder."

7. Which of the following are *parallel?*
    (a) the opposite sides of a square   (c) the letters A, E, and O
    (b) the three sides of a triangle   (d) the numbers 1, 2, and 3

8. Which of the following would you expect to be *graceful?*
    (a) a beginning skier   (c) a Broadway dancer
    (b) an Olympic diver   (d) an Olympic skater

4D Completing the Thought

Read each sentence below and fill in the blank with the correct word (or a form of the word) from the word list.

1. Rick Lee put it in writing that he would play for the White Sox for one season. He signed a one-year _____.

2. Marcie begged her parents to let her have a puppy and promised faithfully that she would take care of it. She was _____ to have a pet.

3. Manuel stood up and quickly rattled off the names of all fifty states in alphabetical order. He could _____ the names from memory.

4. Ms. Wise is going to visit her sister in Milwaukee, but she hopes to be back by 7:30 tonight. She wants to _____ the school committee meeting.

5. Wilma had many wonderful visits to her grandmother's house in Queens. She _____ those memories.

6. Massachusetts dog owners must now pay $50 yearly for each animal. The state _____ a tax on every dog.

7. His parents raised William's allowance from five dollars to five-fifty a week. He thought it was too _____ an increase.

8. Mr. Larrabee asked for a moment of silence, then bowed his head and gave thanks for the wonderful meal that had been laid before them. He said _____.

9. *The Gazette* ran a front-page story giving details of bribes contractors paid City Hall for work on the new parking garage. The paper's reporters _____ the crime.

attend
cherish
contract
eager
expose
grace
impose
modest
recite

4E Narrative   *Read the narrative below, then complete the exercise that follows.*

ONE STEP AT A TIME

Sucheng Chan was an **active** child who loved to run outside and play with the other children in the village in China where she was born. But in 1943, when she was four years old, she **contracted** polio, a childhood disease that can make people very sick and often causes **paralysis**. The muscles in her legs slowly wasted away, and she could no longer run or even walk. The doctors were **pessimistic** about her chances of living more than a year or two. They did not know what a determined person Sucheng Chan was.

After lying helplessly in bed for three years, Sucheng Chan surprised her mother one day by asking her to set up some chairs in two **parallel** lines, their backs facing. She then forced herself out of bed and made her way between the chairs, using their backs as support. She did this time after time, her body aching from many falls.

China was at war with Japan during these years, and Sucheng Chan's father was serving in the army, unable to see his family. He **cherished** his daughter, and it saddened him that he could not give her the comfort and support she needed. When the war ended and he returned home, he was **astounded** to see Sucheng Chan walk up to him and welcome him. Her movements were jerky and not at all **graceful,** but to her father there had never been such a beautiful sight.

Sucheng Chan had always been a bright child who was **eager** to go to school. But in those days in China education was not free, and her parents had only a **modest** income. Sucheng Chan was eight years old before they had saved enough money for her to **attend** the American school in Shanghai. There she learned to speak English and began a lifelong study of Asian history.

In 1948, at the end of Sucheng Chan's first year in school, China's government became communist. The new government **imposed** strict rules forbidding contact with foreigners. One result of these measures was that the American school was closed. Sucheng Chan and her parents grew increasingly unhappy. They decided to leave China and settle in Malaysia.

Sucheng Chan's teenage years, which she spent in a Malaysian high school, were the happiest of her life. She did very well in school and took piano lessons, sometimes giving **recitals** for visitors. Once, while walking across the stage, her legs gave way and she fell. She heard a voice say, "Ayah! A baikah (cripple) should not **expose** herself like that." Sucheng Chan's **response** was to struggle to her feet, walk to the piano, sit down, and play so beautifully that the audience was moved to tears.

After graduating from high school, Sucheng Chan went on to win scholarships to the University of Hawaii. She later became a professor of history and director of

Asian American studies at the University of California, Santa Barbara, leading a full and **active** life. Doctors told her that she might need a wheelchair by the time she was forty because polio can come back, causing more damage to muscles. They were right. But, she said, "I use it only when I am *not* in a hurry."

Answer each of the following questions in a sentence. If a question does not contain a vocabulary word, use a vocabulary word in your answer. Use each word only once. Questions and answers will then contain all fifteen words (or forms of the words) from this lesson's word list.

1. Why didn't Sucheng Chan go to school until she was eight?

   _____

2. Why did it become impossible for Sucheng Chan to run outside and play?

   _____

3. Did her doctors expect Sucheng Chan to get better?

   _____

4. What usually happens to people who **contract** polio?

   _____

5. What is the meaning of **active** as it is used in the narrative?

   _____

6. How does the narrative suggest that her father often thought of Sucheng Chan while he was away?

   _____

7. Why was Sucheng Chan's father **astounded** when he saw his daughter after the war?

   _____

8. Why wasn't Sucheng Chan **graceful**?

   _____

9. How did Sucheng Chan feel about going to school?

   _____

10. What is the meaning of **attend** as it is used in the narrative?

   _____

11. Why don't **parallel** lines ever meet?

_____

12. Why do you think China **imposed** rules against contact with foreigners?

_____

13. How can you tell that Sucheng Chan played the piano well?

_____

14. What did the person who remarked that Sucheng Chan "should not **expose** herself like that" expect her to do?

_____

15. What might Sucheng Chan's **response** have been if she were not such a determined person?

_____

WORDLY WISE

Antonyms are words that are opposite in meaning. The antonym of *contract* in its meaning of "to make or become smaller" is *expand*. Metals contract as they get colder; they expand as they get warmer.

Pessimist and *optimist* are another pair of antonyms. An *optimist* has a cheerful outlook on life and expects things to go well. *Pessimist* is formed from the Latin word *pessimus,* which means "worst." *Optimist* is formed from the Latin word *optimus,* which means "best." There is a saying that a pessimist is a person who looks upon the glass as being half-empty; an optimist is a person who looks upon it as being half-full.

CROSSWORD PUZZLE

Solve the crossword puzzle below by studying the clues and filling in the answer boxes. Clues followed by a number are definitions of words in Lessons 1—4. The number gives the word list in which the answer to the clue appears.

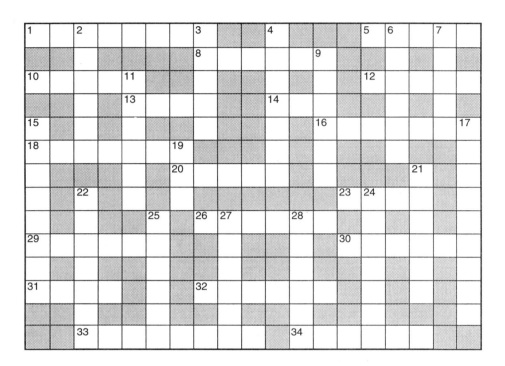

Clues Across

1. Having no missing parts (1)
5. To rot (2)
8. To be present at (4)
10. To speak (1)
12. The Atlantic _____
13. To make less painful (1)
14. One, _____ , three
16. To make larger or better (1)
18. To make ready (3)
20. A group of trees growing together (2)
23. A stomach _____
26. To burn slightly (2)
29. Lively; quick; busy (4)
30. To cause feelings of fear, worry, or surprise (1)
31. To greet or welcome (1)
32. A hole or tunnel dug by an animal (3)
33. Very high (2)
34. Very strict or harsh (3)

Clues Down

2. Fully grown (2)
3. Wanting very much to do or get (4)
4. To dare to do, to go, or to say (3)
6. To go beyond something (2)
7. The _____ is a famous fort in San Antonio.
9. To draw in an aimless kind of way
11. Something said or expressed (1)
15. To come closer (3)
17. Loss of ability to do or feel (4)
19. Something laid by a bird
21. A paper allowing a person to do something (2)
22. One who loves and supports his country (1)
24. The average weather conditions of an area (2)
25. To lie in a sheltered, partly hidden place (3)
27. A row of figures running down a page (2)
28. Red and blue for example

Lesson 5

Word List

Study the definitions of the words below; then do the exercises for the lesson.

abrupt   *adj.* Happening suddenly, without warning.
[When the bus made an *abrupt* stop, several people were thrown off balance.]

achieve   *v.* To do what one sets out to do.
[Even though she was blind and deaf, Helen Keller *achieved* her goal of graduating from college.]
achievement *n.* Something done that takes skill or effort.
[Landing astronauts on the moon was a great *achievement*.]

attempt   *v.* To try; to make an effort.
[When I *attempted* to leave class early, the teacher asked me to wait until the period was over.]
n. A try.
[The athlete cleared the bar in the high jump on her third *attempt*.]

contempt   *n.* A feeling that someone or something is bad or unworthy.
[Their classmates felt nothing but *contempt* for those who refused to help the new student.]

entertain   *v.* 1. To interest and amuse.
[My little brother Ramon *entertained* himself for hours with his new paints.]
2. To have guests.
[We *entertained* some old friends on Thanksgiving weekend.]
3. To have in mind.
[Lin is *entertaining* the idea of going to soccer camp next summer.]

glimpse   *v.* To get a quick look at.
[I *glimpsed* Angela in the crowd at the game, but then I lost sight of her.]
n. A quick or hasty look.
[I was thrilled to get a *glimpse* of Pavarotti leaving the opera house.]

mock   *v.* To make fun of.
[Cinderella's stepsisters *mocked* her for thinking she could go to the ball.]
adj. Not real; pretended.
[*Mock* turtle soup is really made of veal broth, not turtle meat.]

persist   *v.* 1. To keep on doing or trying.
[In spite of many falls on the ice, I *persisted* and finally did a figure-eight.]
2. To go on and on.
[If this rain *persists,* we'll have to cut our vacation short.]
persistence *n.* Sticking to something; not giving up.
[Emil's *persistence* was rewarded when the tenth law school he applied to accepted him.]
persistent *adj.* Refusing to give up.
[The *persistent* reporter kept asking questions until she had found out all there was to know about the case.]

persuade	*v.* To win someone over by arguing or asking. [Frank finally *persuaded* me to read *Tom Sawyer*.] **persuasive** *adj.* Having the power to persuade. [Mary was so *persuasive* that we agreed to help her paint her room.]
phase	*n.* A stage in a series of changes. [The full moon is one of the *phases* of the moon.]
quaint	*adj.* Odd or unusual in a pleasing or old-fashioned way. [Wooden shoes seem *quaint* to Americans, but not to the people of Holland.]
recall	*v.* 1. To remember. [Do you *recall* what time we left for the soccer game?] 2. To call or take back. [The manufacturer *recalled* the cars because of a problem in the steering.]
reject	*v.* To refuse to accept or use. [The school board *rejected* the plan for the new gym because its cost was excessive.] *n.* Something that falls short of what is acceptable. [Peter buys factory *rejects* at the pottery store for much less than the price of perfect pieces.]
revise	*v.* 1. To go over carefully in order to correct or improve. [I don't like to *revise* my stories, but I have to admit they get better when I do.] 2. To change in order to bring up to date. [The publishers of that dictionary *revise* it every eight or ten years.]
sensitive	*adj.* 1. Quick to notice or feel. [My doctor is very *sensitive* to my feelings.] 2. Easily affected by even slight change. [Film used in cameras is very *sensitive* to light.]

5A Finding Meanings

Choose two phrases to form a sentence that correctly uses a word from Word List 5. Write each sentence in the space provided.

1. (a) one stage in a process.
   (b) something overheard.
   (c) A glimpse is
   (d) A phase is

_____

2. (a) An achievement is
   (b) something done by making an effort.
   (c) Contempt is
   (d) something that is changed.

_____

3. (a) loud noise.
   (b) quick look.
   (c) A glimpse is a
   (d) A reject is a

_____

4. (a) Persistence is   (c) a feeling that something is unworthy.
   (b) Contempt is   (d) a wish to do better.

5. (a) that is not accepted.   (c) An attempt is something
   (b) that goes on longer than expected.   (d) A reject is something

6. (a) Sensitive people   (c) are skilled at getting their ideas across.
   (b) expect the worst to happen.   (d) Persuasive people

7. (a) To attempt something is to   (c) take it back.
   (b) try to do it.   (d) To revise something is to

8. (a) give up.   (c) refuse to give up.
   (b) To persist is to   (d) To recall is to

9. (a) To mock an idea is to   (c) To entertain an idea is to
   (b) give it serious thought.   (d) keep it to oneself.

10. (a) To recall something is   (c) to take it back.
    (b) To revise something is   (d) to throw it with force.

5B Just the Right Word

Improve each of the following sentences by crossing out the italicized phrase and replacing it with a word (or a form of the word) from Lesson 5.

1. This thermometer is very *quick to show changes* to the temperature.

2. His top hat and long cape seemed *pleasingly old-fashioned* to the audience.

3. The *unexpectedly sudden* change in the weather surprised everyone.

4. She is so hard-working that no one doubts that she will work long and hard to *reach her goal of* finishing her autobiography.

5. We *had people staying with us* almost every weekend last summer.

6. If the fog *goes on for a long time,* the plane will be unable to leave on time.

7. The coach *made fun of* the shortstop's unusual way of running.

8. I *caught a quick look at* him through the window of the bus.

9. She needs to *make changes in* her speech before she gives it.

10. Each *stage in the series of changes* must be carefully planned or the project will fail.

5C Applying Meanings

Circle the letter of each correct answer to the questions below. Each question has from one to four correct answers.

1. Which of the following can be *sensitive?*
   (a) a person's clothing
   (b) a person's hearing
   (c) a person's feelings
   (d) a person's skin

2. Which of the following might a person think *quaint?*
   (a) a full moon
   (b) an old Valentine card
   (c) a hundred-year-old toy
   (d) pictures in a 1910 book of fairy tales

3. Which of the following might a person *glimpse?*
   (a) someone leaving a crowded room
   (b) a letter someone is trying to hide
   (c) a loud noise
   (d) a strange smell

4. Which of the following can a person *achieve?*
   (a) a goal one sets for oneself
   (b) a calm frame of mind
   (c) curly hair
   (d) high marks on a test

5. Which of the following would you probably *reject?*
   (a) a chance to attend college
   (b) an offer of a ride from a stranger
   (c) bad advice
   (d) an unworkable plan

6. Which of the following might be *persistent?*
   (a) a flash of lightning
   (b) cold and rainy weather
   (c) a back pain
   (d) a bad smell

7. Which of the following might a person *revise?*
   (a) a speech before giving it   (c) a set of calculations
   (b) a paper before handing it in   (d) a friend's opinion

8. Which of the following might be *entertaining?*
   (a) a magician's tricks   (c) a bus timetable
   (b) a football game   (d) an aching tooth

5D Completing the Thought

Read each sentence below and fill in the blank with the correct word (or a form of the word) from the word list.

1. Marie keeps her skin covered when out in the sun since she burns easily. Her skin is very _____.

2. At first, the Ramirezes were eager to sell their house, but then they decided not to. They _____ the idea.

3. Ms. Abernathy was astounded when her mother suddenly jumped up and ran out the door. She left very _____.

4. Law students are supposed to behave as though the trial they hold at the end of the year is a real one, even though it isn't. Their _____ trial is a kind of exam.

| abrupt |
| attempt |
| contempt |
| mock |
| persist |
| persuade |
| recall |
| reject |
| revise |
| sensitive |

5. Elizabeth couldn't remember where Karachi is when she saw the question on the test. Suddenly, however, she _____ the answer.

6. WorldWide Books makes sure that the information in the travel books it publishes is always up to date. They _____ their books each year.

7. Carlita had never played basketball before, but she was really lucky. She got a basket on her first _____.

8. After writing letter after letter to our Congressman asking for his views on the situation in the Middle East, my mother received a long reply. Her _____ was finally rewarded.

9. Alexei was upset by Robert's cruel remarks, but he decided not to lower himself by responding to them. He treated Robert's remarks with _____.

10. Because my aunt played the clarinet she kept trying to get me to take lessons. Whenever she came to visit she'd try to _____ me to start.

5E Narrative   *Read the narrative below; then complete the exercise that follows.*

A LIFE THAT CHANGED

In Hans Christian Andersen's famous story, "The Ugly Duckling," a little duckling who looks different from the other ducks changes magically into a beautiful swan. From a brief **glimpse** into the life of the author, we learn that Andersen, himself, changed dramatically, but not through magic.

Hans Christian Andersen was born in Denmark in 1805. His father was a shoemaker who struggled to make a living. Hans always felt loved by his parents, and had a happy childhood. He had no brothers or sisters, and he was a **sensitive** child who lived in a private world of his own. His greatest joy was a toy theater his father made for him. The little boy **entertained** his parents by putting on plays, dressing the people of his little toy theater in **quaint** clothes that he made himself.

When Hans was eleven his father died, and the young boy's life changed **abruptly**. He had to go to work, but he failed at every job he **attempted**. His fellow workers could not understand the strange boy who spent all his time daydreaming, and they treated him with **contempt, mocking** him and making his life miserable. When he was fourteen, Hans **persuaded** his mother to let him go to the big city of Copenhagen, where he tried to get work as an actor, but was unsuccessful. He also tried dancing and singing, but he was not very good at these either. He tried writing plays, but they were **rejected** by theater owners. In this **phase** of his life, he didn't seem to fit in anywhere.

But Hans Christian Andersen **persisted** in his efforts to be a writer. Over the next fifteen years he wrote poems, travel articles, and novels, as well as plays. He worked very hard, taking care to **revise** each sentence carefully until he got the words just right. No one paid much attention to his work, however, until he began writing fairy tales. He did not have to search for ideas for these; all he had to do was **recall** the stories his father had told him when he was a little boy. He wrote more than a hundred and fifty wonderful fairy tales, at last **achieving** fame and becoming one of the best loved writers in the world. You will read one of his stories in the next lesson.

Answer each of the following questions in a sentence. If a question does not contain a vocabulary word, use a vocabulary word in your answer. Use each word only once. Questions and answers will then contain all fifteen words (or forms of the words) from this lesson's word list.

1. How do you think a **sensitive** person like Andersen might have responded to cruel remarks?

   _____

2. What was one of Andersen's favorite childhood activities?

   _____

3. Why did the people in Hans's toy theater look so charmingly old-fashioned?

   _____

4. What caused an **abrupt** change in Andersen's life when he was a child?

   _____

5. What might Andersen have said to **persuade** his mother to let him go to Copenhagen?

   _____

6. Why must Andersen's mother have been pessimistic about his chances of success?

   _____

7. How do you know that Andersen was not popular with his fellow workers?

   _____

8. Was Andersen's playwriting successful?

   _____

9. What jobs did Hans try during the **phase** of his life when he didn't fit in anywhere?

   _____

10. In your opinion, what was Andersen's greatest **achievement**?

   _____

11. What helped give him ideas for stories?

   _____

12. How can you tell that Andersen was usually not satisfied with his first version of a story?

   _____

13. What quality did Andersen have that helped him succeed?

_____

14. Why do you think the people Andersen worked with **mocked** him?

_____

15. Why might the story of the Ugly Duckling be of special interest to Andersen's readers?

_____

WORDLY WISE

The Latin *abruptus* means "broken" and *forms* the root of the adjective **abrupt**. If there is an *abrupt* end to something - a speech, for example - it means it was *broken* off suddenly and unexpectedly. Other words formed from this root include *interrupt* (When you *interrupt* a conversation, you *break* into it.) and *disrupt* (If you *disrupt* a meeting, you *break* it up.).

Lesson 6

Word List

Study the definitions of the words below; then do the exercises for the lesson.

applaud
v. 1. To show approval, especially by clapping hands.
[The audience *applauded* until the cast came back on stage to take another bow.]
applause *n.* The showing of approval or enjoyment by cheering or clapping.
[The theater lights came on after the *applause* had died down.]

crafty
adj. Skilled at tricking others.
[Templeton, the *crafty* and mean-spirited rat in *Charlotte's Web,* adds humor to the book.]

disclose
v. 1. To make known.
[The judge told the reporter she must *disclose* the name of the person who gave her the story or be held in contempt of court.]

drab
adj. Dull and without color; not cheerful or colorful.
[A sparrow is a *drab* little bird compared to a male cardinal.]

entire
adj. Having nothing left out; whole; complete.
[I recited the *entire* Robert Frost poem from memory].

exclaim
v. To speak suddenly and with strong feeling.
["Today was the worst day of my life!" she *exclaimed.*]
exclamation *n.* A sharp cry of strong feeling.
[Grandpa's *exclamation* of pain sent me rushing to his side.]

exquisite
adj. Finely done or made; very beautiful.
[The *exquisite* wood carvings on the museum door came from an Egyptian temple.]

intend
v. To plan; to have in mind.
[I *intend* to give a piano recital on Monday.]
intention *n.* An aim, plan, or purpose.
[It was Thea's *intention* to open a bookstore, but she decided to go to engineering school instead.]

jeer
v. To speak or cry out in scorn; to mock.
[My brother told me to ignore them if the older boys *jeered* when I sang.]
n. Something said that is meant to hurt or insult.
[An umpire soon learns to ignore the *jeers* of the crowd.]

peer
v. To look closely; to stare, especially at something that is hard to see or to understand.
[Shining green eyes *peered* at us through a narrow opening in the door.]

progress   *n.* ('pro gress) 1. Moving toward a goal.
[The stormy sea slowed the small boat's *progress*.]
2. An improvement.
[I am finally making some *progress* mastering the new computer program.]
v. (pro 'gress) 1. To move forward.
[Work on the new bridge *progressed* at a faster pace when the weather improved.]
2. To advance to a higher stage; to improve.
[Manuel *progressed* so fast on the tuba that he got into the school band.]

refine   *v.* To make pure by removing all unwanted matter.
[We take oil from deep inside the earth and *refine* it into gasoline.]
refined   *adj.* 1. In a pure state.
[When flour is *refined*, a lot of the wheat germ is lost.]
2. Having good manners and good taste.
[He was a noisy and rude boy, but as young man he is gentle and *refined*.]

scoundrel   *n.* A mean or wicked person.
[Thank heavens the police caught the *scoundrel* who stole my wallet.]

uneasy   *adj.* Not comfortable; worried or nervous.
[I felt *uneasy* walking down the dark street until I observed a police officer on the corner.]

vain   *adj.* 1. Having too high an opinion of one's looks or achievements.
[Charlie is so *vain* he has a full-length mirror in every room.]
2. Without success.
[The firefighters made a *vain* attempt to keep the fire from spreading.]
in vain   *adv.* Without success or result; useless.
[All my hand-waving was *in vain*—the teacher never called on me.]

6A Finding Meanings

Choose two phrases to form a sentence that correctly uses a word from Word List 6. Write each sentence in the space provided.

1. (a) one that is complete.   (c) one that is not broken.
   (b) An entire set is   (d) An exquisite set is

_____

2. (a) Crafty persons are those who   (c) Vain persons are those who
   (b) think too highly of themselves. (d) do not think well of themselves.

_____

3. (a) beautiful to look at.   (c) An exquisite fabric is one that is
   (b) A drab fabric is one that is   (d) hidden from view.

_____

4. (a) A jeer is   (c) a small hand tool.
   (b) A scoundrel is   (d) a dishonest person.

---

5. (a) easily hurt or upset.   (c) Refined people are
   (b) dull and uninteresting.   (d) Drab colors are

---

6. (a) A crafty person is one who   (c) refuses to give up easily.
   (b) An uneasy person is one who   (d) is skilled at tricking people.

---

7. (a) An exclamation is   (c) something said with strong feeling.
   (b) An intention is   (d) a feeling of not being wanted.

---

8. (a) take it back.   (c) To refine something is to
   (b) To disclose something is to   (d) make it pure.

---

9. (a) An intention is something   (c) one denies having done.
   (b) one plans to do.   (d) A jeer is something

---

10. (a) come into view.   (c) To progress is to
    (b) To peer is to   (d) move forward.

---

11. (a) be hard to get along with.   (c) To be uneasy is to
    (b) To be applauded is to   (d) be worried or nervous.

6B Just the Right word

Improve each of the following sentences by crossing out the italicized phrase and replacing it with a word or (a form of the word) from Word List 6.

1. Josh *looked closely* at the faded sign but was unable to make out what it said.

2. Remi was eager to renew the contract, but all her efforts were *not met with success.*

3. A *well-mannered* person does not try to talk with his mouth full.

4. Their *rude and unkind remarks* made them very unpopular with the team.

5. Icy road conditions slowed our *forward movement* through town.

6. "Now I understand!" Einstein *said suddenly, with strong feeling,* as he jumped up.

7. He was so *good at tricking people* that those he fooled did not even know it.

8. My mother is getting ready to *tell the public* that she is going to run for Congress.

9. The cast knew *Oklahoma!* was a success when they heard the loud *cheering and clapping.*

6C Applying Meanings

Circle the letter of each correct answer to the questions below. A question may have more than one correct answer.

1. Which of the following might look *drab?*
   (a) a dark suit of clothes   (c) a freshly painted room
   (b) a rainbow   (d) a circus clown

2. Which of the following are *entire* words?
   (a) father   (c) s me b dy
   (b) m th r   (d) I

3. Which of the following might be called *exquisite?*
   (a) a wedding dress   (c) a grease spot
   (b) a diamond necklace   (d) a cigarette butt

4. What might cause *jeers* from the crowd at a baseball game?
   (a) an umpire's bad call   (c) a home run
   (b) a win for the home team   (d) a dropped catch

5. Which of the following might someone *peer* at?
   (a) a hard-to-read letter   (c) a loud noise
   (b) a strangely dressed person   (d) an unpleasant smell

6. Which of the following might make a person *uneasy?*
   (a) winning first prize   (c) climbing a tall ladder
   (b) hearing strange noises   (d) being left alone at night

7. Which of the following would it be *vain* to attempt?
   (a) unscrambling an egg   (c) traveling backward in time
   (b) learning Chinese   (d) climbing Mount Everest

8. Which of the following would a person be likely to *applaud?*
   (a) a great achievement   (c) an entertaining show
   (b) a pessimistic remark   (d) a patriotic speech

6D Completing the Thought

Read each sentence below and fill in the blank with the correct word (or a form of the word) from the word list.

1. Sheila told her best friend that she hated to fly. She _____ her fear on the way to the airport.

2. Charles shuffled his feet and couldn't look his father in the eye when he was asked what he had done with the money. He felt very _____.

3. Mrs. Roth can't persuade her daughter to give up her idea of sailing alone across the Atlantic. She _____ to make the trip, no matter what her mother says.

4. Most of the members of the book group agreed that holding monthly meetings was a very good idea. They _____ the decision.

5. Jonathan got his black belt in karate much more quickly than anyone had expected. He made rapid _____.

6. When Mrs. Luzano tried to reach the man she had given her money to, she found that he had given her a false telephone number. "That man is a _____ _____!" she shouted.

applaud
disclose
intend
peer
progress
refine
scoundrel
uneasy
vain
exclaim

7. Jessie pressed her face to the glass, trying to get a better look at the person who was visiting her next-door neighbor. She _____ out the window.

8. While her stepsisters spent hours in front of the mirror, Cinderella dressed quickly. She was not a _____ person.

9. After the water has been boiled off and the maple syrup has been filtered, it is poured into jars and labeled. The _____ syrup is what we get in the store.

10. One of my grandmother's favorite sayings was "Jiminy Crickets!" I used to love hearing this _____.

6E Narrative   *Read the narrative below; then complete the exercise that follows.*

"THE EMPEROR'S NEW CLOTHES"*

Once there was an emperor who was very **vain,** spending hour after hour **peering** at himself in the mirror. Whenever he got new clothes he would gather his ministers around him so that they could tell him how wonderful he looked.

One day, two men who said they were master tailors came to see the emperor. They told him they could make him a suit of clothes so magnificent that everything else he owned would seem **drab.** The cloth would be so unusual that only those with the most **refined** taste would be able to see it. The emperor was foolish enough to believe them and agreed to pay whatever they asked.

The "tailors" started work at once. Every day the emperor sent his ministers to check on their **progress.** Of course, they could see perfectly well that the **crafty** pair were only pretending to weave the cloth and cut it and stitch it, but they didn't dare **disclose** the truth to the emperor. The ministers were afraid to disagree with the emperor because that would be like confessing that they did not have good taste. They felt **uneasy** about lying, but they believed they had no choice. They told the emperor only what he wanted to hear—that his new clothes were the most **exquisite** they had ever seen.

When the two **scoundrels** told the emperor that their work was complete, he was so excited that he announced that the next day would be a public holiday. He **intended** to walk through the streets of the town in his new clothes so that everyone could admire him. The next morning, the "tailors" carefully laid out the emperor's new clothes and began helping him dress. The ministers gathered around to watch,

*This narrative is a retelling of the popular fairy tale by Hans Christian Andersen.

and there were loud **exclamations** of delight when the emperor, turning this way and that, at last stood proudly before them dressed only in his underwear.

Officers of the palace guard had been up since before dawn making sure that the townspeople turned out to **applaud** the emperor as he went by. The **entire** town lined the streets to see him. Under the watchful eyes of the officers, the people cheered and waved flags, and the emperor loved every minute of it. But then something unexpected happened. Above the roar of the crowd, the emperor heard a child's voice saying, "Look! The emperor has no clothes!" The cry was at once taken up by the crowd. "THE EMPEROR HAS NO CLOTHES! THE EMPEROR HAS NO CLOTHES!"

The emperor looked down at himself and saw that it was true. He knew that he had been tricked. Feeling very foolish, he ran back to the palace as fast as he could, the **jeers** of the crowd ringing in his ears.

Answer each of the following questions in a sentence. If a question does not contain a vocabulary word, use a vocabulary word in your answer. Use each word only once. Questions and answers will then contain all fifteen words (or forms of the words) from this lesson's word list.

1. What did the emperor do with his time?

   _____

2. Why might the emperor have been tempted to get rid of all his old clothes after he talked to his tailors?

   _____

3. How would you describe **refined** taste?

   _____

4. Why was it impossible to judge how the tailors' work was **progressing**?

   _____

5. Why does the narrative refer to the two tailors as **scoundrels**?

   _____

6. Who finally **disclosed** the truth to the emperor?

   _____

7. Why were the ministers **uneasy**?

8. What did the ministers tell the emperor?

   _____

9. What do you think the ministers thought of the two tailors?

   _____

10. What do you think was the tailors' **intention** in tricking the emperor?

    _____

11. Why did the ministers **exclaim** in delight?

    _____

12. Why do you think the child might have deserved the crowd's **applause**?

    _____

13. Why did the **entire** town show up to see the emperor?

    _____

14. Why did the emperor run back to the palace?

    _____

15. What vocabulary word describes the emperor perfectly? Why?

    _____

WORDLY WISE

The adjective **drab** is also the name of a color - a light, green-brown. (U.S. soldiers wear olive-*drab* clothing.) *Drab* is also a noun meaning "a small amount," but it is found only in the phrase "in dribs and drabs," meaning a little bit at a time. (Instead of paying me the money all at once, they gave it to me *in dribs and drabs*.)

◆ ◆ ◆ ◆ ◆ ◆ ◆

As well as being a verb, **peer** is also a noun. It means "an equal; a person of the same rank or position as another." For example, "Those sixth graders are my *peers*. We all are in the same class." Or, to say that Daniel Webster had no *peer* as a public speaker is to say that no one could equal him in the art of public speaking. A *peer* is also the name for a member of the English House of Lords.

Lesson 7

Word List

Study the definitions of the words below; then do the exercises for the lesson.

alter   *v.* To change in some way; to make or become different.
[Let's *alter* our uniforms so they will fit better.]
alteration   *n.* A change.
[Please don't make any *alterations* in my newspaper column.]

confuse   *v.* 1. To make or become unclear or mixed up in the mind.
[That math problem totally *confused* me.]
2. To mistake one person or thing for another.
[I always *confuse* Sally with her twin sister Samantha.]
confusing   *adj.* Hard to follow or understand; unclear.
[The play was *confusing* at first, but I began to understand it in the second act.]
confusion   *n.* A state of disorder.
[After the playoff game, the dressing room was total *confusion*.]

distribute   *v.* 1. To give out; to divide among several or many.
[Ahmed *distributed* programs before the concert.]
2. To be spread over.
[Small parks are *distributed* throughout London.]

eject   *v.* To force or throw out.
[When the seventh graders refused to listen, the coach *ejected* them from the team meeting.]

embrace   *v.* 1. To hold closely in one's arms; to hug.
[My parents *embraced* me when I got off the plane.]
2. To take up seriously.
[We *embraced* the idea of smaller classes, but lacked the teachers to carry it out.]
n. A hug.
[At the end of the movie, the hero and the heroine were locked in an *embrace*.]

equip   *v.* To provide with what is needed.
[Many cars are now *equipped* with airbags.]
equipment   *n.* Things that are needed for some activity.
[Sarah got all her camping *equipment* on sale.]

flexible   *adj.* 1. Able to bend easily.
[Dancers and gymnasts have very *flexible* bodies.]
2. Able to adjust to new or different situations.
[Antonio is so *flexible* he can get along with anyone.]

instant   *n.* A moment; a very short period of time.
[It took Luis only an *instant* to figure out the answer.]
adj. Happening or done at once; quick.
[He gave an *instant* "yes" to her offer.]

keen   *adj.* 1. Having a sharp edge.
[The *keen* blade of the knife sliced through the thick rope with ease.]
2. Showing a strong interest; eager.
[Marta signed up for lessons because she was *keen* to learn to play the guitar.]
3. Having sharp senses; quick to understand.
[With her *keen* mind she was able to master physics with ease.]

limp   *v.* To walk lamely or in an uneven way.
[I *limped* for two weeks after I fell on the ice.]
n. An uneven or lopsided walk.
[She walked very fast, in spite of her *limp*.]
adj. Not stiff or firm.
[His handshake was as *limp* as a wet rag].

scurry   *v.* To move quickly, with rapid little steps.
[The chipmunk *scurried* up the tree as we approached.]

seize   *v.* 1. To grasp suddenly; to grab hold of.
[He *seized* my hand and begged me not to go.]
2. To take by force of the law.
[The government can *seize* many of the things you own if you do not pay your taxes.]

shallow   *adj.* 1. Not deep.
[We went wading in a *shallow* stream.]
2. With little seriousness or deep thought.
[He tried to sound intelligent, but his arguments were really quite *shallow*.]

surround   *v.* To enclose on all sides.
[The prison was *surrounded* by a high fence.]
surroundings   *n. pl.* The things or conditions around a person or place.
[The hotel's peaceful *surroundings* made it a perfect place to relax.]

victim   *n.* One who is hurt, killed, or suffers.
[The scoundrel tried to deny that he had cheated his *victims* of their life savings.]

7A Finding Meanings

Choose two phrases to form a sentence that correctly uses a word from Word List 7. Write each sentence in the space provided.

1. (a) Surroundings are
   (b) Alterations are
   (c) needed items for some activity.
   (d) the conditions around one.

_____

2. (a) To eject a group is to
   (b) provide it with what is needed.
   (c) To equip a group is to
   (d) allow it to take part.

_____

3. (a) throw them out.   (c) take them by force.
    (b) To seize papers is to   (d) To distribute papers is to

4. (a) To be flexible is to be   (c) unwilling to change your mind.
    (b) To be keen is to be   (d) agreeable to any sudden change of plan.

5. (a) Alteration is   (c) a state of being mixed up.
    (b) unwillingness to change.   (d) Confusion is

6. (a) Victims are   (c) persons who avoid injury.
    (b) persons who are hurt.   (d) Embraces are

7. (a) A limp handshake is   (c) is very sensitive.
    (b) A keen sense of smell   (d) very eager.

8. (a) a hug.   (c) An instant is
    (b) An embrace is   (d) a handshake.

9. (a) To limp is to   (c) To scurry is to
    (b) grasp firmly.   (d) walk unevenly.

10. (a) to hold onto them.   (c) To distribute things is
    (b) to give them out.   (d) To confuse things is

7B Just the Right Word

Improve each of the following sentences by crossing out the italicized phrase and replacing it with a word (or a form of the word) from Word List 7.

1. The dog's *uneven walk* was caused by a thorn in its left front paw.

2. I *opened my arms and held* my cousin, whom I hadn't seen in two years.

3. Stay close to shore where the water is *not very deep*.

4. My cat jumped as a mouse *ran with quick little steps* across the kitchen floor.

5. I caught a glimpse of the president in the parade for just a(n) *very short period of time*.

6. This map is very *hard to follow* because some of the streets aren't named.

7. With just a slight *change in form* of the shape of the number, a 3 becomes an 8.

8. The boxes of food were *given out* in time for Thanksgiving.

9. My whole family *gathered around* me, singing "Happy Birthday."

10. Luckily, the pilot was *thrown with great force* from the plane before it crashed.

7C Applying Meanings

Circle the letter of each correct answer to the questions below. A question may have more than one correct answer.

1. Which of the following can be *altered?*
   (a) one's plans
   (b) today's date
   (c) a dress's hemline
   (d) one's age

2. Which of the following are *flexible?*
   (a) a sewing needle
   (b) a garden hose
   (c) a dancer's body
   (d) a length of cooked spaghetti

3. Which of the following could be given in an *instant?*
   (a) a yes-or-no answer
   (b) a nod of agreement
   (c) a ten-page report
   (d) a smile of welcome

4. Which of the following might feel *limp?*
   (a) a sheet of wet cardboard   (c) a sheet of ice
   (b) a sleeping child   (d) a sheet of plywood

5. Which of the following could *scurry?*
   (a) a spider   (c) an elephant
   (b) a whale   (d) a mouse

6. Which of the following could be *seized?*
   (a) a person's arm   (c) a sneeze
   (b) a person's boat   (d) a puff of smoke

7. Which of the following could be *shallow?*
   (a) a stick   (c) a person's thinking
   (b) a hole   (d) a pond

8. Which of the following might be *keen?*
   (a) a pessimist   (c) a hammer
   (b) a razor blade   (d) a dog's hearing

7D Completing the Thought

Read each sentence below and fill in the blank with the correct word (or a form of the word) from the word list.

1. There were so many questions being thrown at her that Marjorie would hardly have known the answer if someone had asked her name. She was very _____ by it all.

2. Bobby dressed up as Uncle Sam and gave each child a flag at the Fourth of July picnic. He _____ them to everyone under sixteen.

3. When Carole and Nicole went rock climbing, they had to carry everything they needed. They put their _____ in backpacks.

4. Someone had written the letters O N after the name Wilkins. The name had been _____ to read Wilkinson.

5. Mr. Rubin kept calling officials in Japan to see if they had any news about his son. He was afraid he might be a _____ of the earthquake.

6. Camilla Knowles's latest book shot to the top of the bestseller list as soon as it was published. The novel was an _____ success.

Word List
alter
confuse
distribute
eject
embrace
equip
instant
keen
surround
victim

7. The batter kept arguing with the pitcher, so the umpire said he could no longer take part in the game. He _____ him in the fourth inning.

8. Kabir could always figure out the answers to the hardest math problems. He had a very _____ mind.

9. The workers liked the plan for a shorter work week even though it would result in a modest reduction in wages. They _____ the new idea right away.

10. We have to keep the raccoons away from our tomato plants, so we're putting up a wire fence. It will _____ the garden.

7E Narrative

Read the narrative below; then complete the exercise that follows.

ARMED BUT NOT DANGEROUS

What is sometimes green, sometimes brown, sometimes gray, sometimes a mixture of all three colors, and has one head and eight arms? Here is a clue: the Greek word for eight is *okto*. If you guessed octopus, you're right!

The octopus lives in holes or openings in the rocky bottom of the sea, where it protects itself from its enemies by changing its color to match its **surroundings.** In seaweed it can turn green; on sand it can turn brown; against rocks it can turn gray. For example, if it is attacked by a shark it can change its color in an **instant** in order to blend into the background. The surprised shark is left wondering where it went. It can also protect itself by **ejecting** a large blob of black ink-like liquid that acts as a screen. This **confuses** its attacker, who may go after the dark blob, giving the octopus a chance to escape.

Because it has no bones, an octopus can easily **alter** its shape; it can then force its way inside empty shells or under rocks or into very narrow openings. To be even safer, it may cover itself with stones or shells.

The octopus's eight rubbery arms are very **flexible** and can easily be wrapped around even quite small objects. Each arm is **equipped** with two rows of fleshy, deeply set suckers that give it a powerful grip. The octopus uses its arms to **seize** other animals such as crabs and lobsters as they **scurry** along the sea floor. It can then use the two strong, horny beaks in its mouth to crack open the shell of its **victim.**

The octopus has **keen** eyesight, which it needs because it hunts mostly at night. It has a large brain for its size, and it makes full use of its intelligence in its efforts to catch food. For example, if an octopus cannot open a clam, it will wait until the clam opens itself. When it does, the octopus will put a stone between the two shells so that they cannot close. Then it can get at the juicy clam without having to struggle.

There are many different kinds of octopuses, and they are widely **distributed** throughout the world's oceans. They live mostly in warm, **shallow** water, not far from shore. The smallest ones grow to be no more than two inches across; the largest ones, which live in the Pacific Ocean, can grow to be thirty feet across, although their body might be only eighteen inches.

If, when swimming in the Pacific, you venture too far from shore, you may find yourself in the **embrace** of one of these creatures. If this should happen to you, it is best not to struggle. If you let your body go **limp,** the octopus will probably let you go. Although movies sometimes show them as terrifying and dangerous monsters, there is no reason to fear them. Around humans, at least, octopuses are usually shy and gentle creatures.

Answer each of the following questions in a sentence. If a question does not contain a vocabulary word, use a vocabulary word in the answer. Use each word only once. Questions and answers will then contain all fifteen words (or forms of the words) from this lesson's word list.

1. Why does an octopus sitting in seaweed turn green?

   _____

2. How long does it take for an octopus to change colors?

   _____

3. Why does the octopus make a "screen"?

   _____

4. How does it make this screen?

   _____

5. How does its lack of a skeleton benefit an octopus?

   _____

6. How would bones in an octopus's arms affect the way it uses them?

   _____

7. How is the octopus **equipped** to grip things?

   _____

8. How do its eight arms help an octopus obtain food?

_____

9. Why might an approaching octopus cause a crab to start **scurrying**?

_____

10. How does an octopus get at the meat in a lobster it has caught?

_____

11. Which of the octopus's senses is especially well-developed?

_____

12. In what parts of the world do octopuses live?

_____

13. Why are you unlikely to see an octopus in the middle of the Atlantic Ocean?

_____

14. Would you be in danger in an octopus's **embrace**? Explain.

_____

15. What is the meaning of **limp**, as used in the narrative?

_____

WORDLY WISE

Alter is a verb; *Altar* (with two *a*'s) is a noun. An *altar* is a table or platform used in churches or temples as a center of worship. A bride and groom may kneel or stand before the altar when they get married. *Alter* and *altar* are homonyms—words that sound alike but have different meanings and spellings.

Flexible means "able to bend or change easily." The antonym of *flexible* is *rigid*, which means "stiff' or "unbending." An iron bar is rigid; if it is heated until it becomes red- or white-hot, it becomes flexible. Both words can be used *literally*, as in the example above, and *figuratively*, as in the examples below. A person who is willing to change plans at the last minute is said to be *flexible*, whereas someone who refuses to make such changes could be called *rigid*. A job with *rigid* hours is one in which the hours of work cannot be changed; a job with *flexible* hours is one in which the hours can be changed easily to suit the needs of the worker or the boss.

Lesson 8

Word List

Study the definitions of the words below; then do the exercises for the lesson.

ancient
adj. Very old; of a long time ago.
[The *ancient* city of Carthage was destroyed by the Romans in 146 B.C.]

century
n. A period of one hundred years.
[The twentieth *century* began on January 1, 1900.]

chamber
n. A large room.
[Chamber music is meant to be played in a *chamber* rather than a much larger concert hall.]
chambers *n. pl.* An office or group of offices.
[Lawyers for both sides met in the judge's *chambers*.]

descend
v. To go or come down.
[The plane slowly *descended* to 2,000 feet.]
descendant *n.* One who has certain persons as one's parents, grandparents, etc.
[The writer Alex Haley was a *descendant* of Kunta Kinte, who was brought to America as a slave from West Africa in 1767.]

entry
n. 1. A way in.
[The thieves gained *entry* through an unlocked window.]
2. Each separate item in a diary or list.
[The next *entry* in her diary simply said, "My brother returned home today after a long absence."]

interior
n. The inside part of something.
[The sun's *interior* is about 150,000 times hotter than boiling water.]
adj. Having to do with the inside part.
[*Interior* doors do not have to be as strongly made as front or back doors.]

intrude
v. To come or go in without permission or welcome.
[I didn't mean to *intrude* on you while you were working].
intrusion *n.* The act of intruding.
["Forgive my *intrusion*," she said as she came in without knocking.]
intruder *n.* One who intrudes.
[People were so unfriendly that I felt like an *intruder* at Jeff's party.]

locate
v. 1. To find.
[Marta *located* the missing books in less than an hour.]
2. To put or to be found in a place.
[We're going to *locate* our office across the street from the school.]
location *n.* The place where something can be found.
[Will you please give me the *location* of the nearest post office?]

passage   *n.* 1. A part of a written work or piece of music.
[The final *passage* of the Mozart mass brought tears to the audience's eyes.]
2. The act or process of passing, as through time or from place to place.
[His deeply-lined face clearly showed the *passage* of time.]
3. A way through which to pass.
[Leon's room was at the end of a long, dimly lit *passage*.]

portion   *n.* 1. A part or share of the whole.
[I got the first *portion* of my allowance last week.]
2. A serving or helping, as of food.
[My diet recommends a four-ounce *portion* of fish or chicken once a day.]

precious   *adj.* 1. Very valuable.
[The necklace was made of diamonds, emeralds, and other *precious* stones.]
2. Much loved.
[She tried in vain to save her *precious* books from the fire.]

quarry   *n.* 1. A deep pit where stone is cut out of the ground.
[The marble for these tiles came from a *quarry* in Vermont.]
2. An animal that is being hunted.
[The hunters gave up the chase when they lost sight of their *quarry*.]

ramp   *n.* A slanted walk or roadway that connects a lower to a higher place.
[The law says that there has to be a *ramp* for those who cannot use the steps.]

spacious   *adj.* Having lots of room.
[The *spacious* kitchen had room for a large round table that seated eight.]

surface   *n.* 1. The outside layer; the top.
[The *surface* of the moon is covered with craters.]
2. An outward look or appearance.
[He seemed cheerful on the *surface*, but I knew how miserable he must have felt to be so cold and wet.]
v. To rise to the top of a body of water.
[The latest submarines can stay underwater for weeks before they need to *surface*.]

8A Finding Meanings

Choose two phrases to form a sentence that correctly uses a word from Word List 8. Write each sentence in the space provided.

1. (a) Interior walls are
   (b) those on the inside.
   (c) those that surround a private area.
   (d) Ancient walls are

_____

2. (a) The passage of something is
   (b) The surface of something is
   (c) its outward appearance.
   (d) its innermost part.

_____

3. (a) A spacious city is one   (c) that is very old.
   (b) that has many visitors.   (d) An ancient city is one

_____

4. (a) A passage is   (c) An intrusion is
   (b) a free pass to a public event.   (d) a way through which to go.

_____

5. (a) Something that is spacious   (c) is very valuable.
   (b) Something that is precious   (d) seems true but is actually false.

_____

6. (a) a sloping walkway.   (c) A ramp is
   (b) A quarry is   (d) a contest.

_____

7. (a) something that gets in the way.   (c) A location is
   (b) a serving of food.   (d) An intrusion is

_____

8. (a) A portion is   (c) a pit from which stone is cut.
   (b) A quarry is   (d) a building open to the public.

_____

9. (a) To locate the stairs is   (c) to go up them.
   (b) to go down them.   (d) To descend the stairs is

_____

10. (a) A portion is   (c) a large room.
    (b) A chamber is   (d) the topmost part.

_____

8B Just the Right Word

Improve each of the following sentences by crossing out the italicized phrase and replacing it with a word (or a form of the word) from Word List 8.

1. Our new apartment has a closet that is *very large*, with room enough to hold a fold-up bed.

2. The United States has enough coal to last for at least a *period of one hundred years*.

3. The divers were searching for the *exact spot* of the sunken treasure.

4. To enter the parking garage you have to drive up the *sloping way* leading to a higher level.

5. The lion's *intended victim* was a young antelope.

6. As we approached the clubhouse, we saw that the only *way in* was blocked by a huge pile of snow.

7. Angela told me she would pay back a *part of the total amount* of the money she owed me by next week.

8. These are the *group of offices* where Senate hearings are held.

9. The *process of passing* of time could be seen in the crumbling stone buildings and rutted streets.

10. A large bullfrog suddenly *rose to the top of the water* and landed on a lilypad.

8C Applying Meanings

Circle the letter of each correct answer to the questions below. A question may have more than one correct answer.

1. Which of the following might be thought of as *precious*?
   (a) a child
   (b) freedom of speech
   (c) a diamond ring
   (d) chewing gum stuck to your shoe

2. Which of the following is *ancient*?
   (a) a joke you've heard before
   (b) last year's calendar
   (c) an Egyptian mummy
   (d) a dinosaur bone

3. Which of the following might an *intruder* at a private meeting be asked to do?
   (a) help give out the notes   (c) leave immediately
   (b) join in the talk   (d) meet the other people

4. Which of the following might a person try to *locate*?
   (a) a problem with a car's engine   (c) a missing relative
   (b) the city of New York on a map   (d) the planet Jupiter

5. Which of the following might you ask for a *portion* of?
   (a) a friend's jacket   (c) cole slaw
   (b) the Sunday newspaper   (d) a friend's age

6. Which of the following has an *interior*?
   (a) a planet   (c) a house
   (b) a sheet of paper   (d) a car

7. Which of the following can be measured in *centuries*?
   (a) the age of the United States   (c) time
   (b) the size of the United States (d) space

8. Which of the following has a *surface*?
   (a) a sharp pain   (c) a lake
   (b) a coat of paint   (d) the sun

8D Completing the Thought

Read each sentence below and fill in the blank with the correct word (or a form of the word) from the word list.

1. Mr. Armitage asked us to translate three pages of Latin for homework. I could do all of it except one difficult
   _____.

2. After attending his first cello lesson, YoYo Ma wrote in his diary that when he grew up he wanted to be a cellist. It turned out to be an important _____.

3. Mrs. Rooney told her son and his wife that storing all their furniture in her basement would not be a problem. It was a _____ room.

4. Our history teacher showed us a model of a trireme, a boat with three rows of oars used over two thousand years ago by the Romans. The trireme was an _____ warship.

ancient
chamber
descend
entry
intrude
locate
passage
portion
precious
spacious

5. Katherine left St. Louis at six a.m. and drove until she reached Kansas City just before noon. Kansas City is _____ 240 miles west of St. Louis.

6. People kept coming into his room without knocking, so René put a sign on the door saying "Keep Out." People were _____ on his privacy.

7. Manuela cut the cake into twelve equal slices and made sure that all the children got a scoop of ice cream with their cake. Everyone had the same size _____.

8. Henry Adams, the writer and historian, came from a distinguished American family. He was a _____ of the sixth president of the United States, John Quincy Adams.

9. Patrick Henry was the American patriot who said, ". . . give me liberty or give me death." He felt that freedom was more _____ than life itself.

10. When the lawyer made an objection to the judge, the judge called her to the bench. He said he'd discuss the matter with her in his _____.

8E Narrative

Read the narrative below; then complete the exercise that follows.

THE GREAT PYRAMID

Over two thousand years ago, a Greek writer named Antipater made a list of what he called the Seven Wonders of the World. The only one of those **ancient** sights that remains today is the Great Pyramid, in Egypt.

The Great Pyramid is **located** just outside Cairo. It was built by one of the earliest kings of Egypt, who intended it to be a tomb, or burial place, for himself. Covering an area bigger than one hundred football fields and standing 450 feet high, it is the largest of the more than sixty pyramids in Egypt. It is made of two and a half million blocks of stone, some of which weigh as much as fifteen tons. Its **surface** was once covered in shining white limestone and was perfectly smooth, but over the **centuries** most of this has been stripped away and very little of it is left.

It may have taken as long as twenty years to build the Great Pyramid. The stone came from nearby, while the white limestone on the outside came from **quarries** near the Nile River. The blocks were floated across on rafts and were then dragged up a **ramp** of earth that was built up in stages as the work progressed. Skilled stonecutters worked all year on the pyramid. Other work was done by farmers, who worked for a **portion** of each year, probably from July to October, when the Nile overflowed its banks and flooded the fields. Workers believed that their king, Cheops, was a god, a **descendant** of the sun god Ra, and that he deserved this magnificent tomb.

The **interior** of the Great Pyramid contains many rooms, connected by **passages** leading to the outside. King Cheops was laid to rest in one of the most **spacious** rooms. The Egyptians believed in a life after death, and so they left food and drink with the king's body as well as many **precious** objects he had used in daily life. The Egyptians believed he would need these in the next world.

The **chamber** in which the dead king lay was closed off with huge granite slabs to keep people from gaining **entry** to it. In spite of this, however, **intruders** later found a way in and stole the gold objects and the jewels that were inside. They even made off with the body! The Great Pyramid failed to keep Cheops's body safe, but it has kept his name alive 4,500 years after his death.

Answer each of the following questions in a sentence. If a question does not contain a vocabulary word, use a vocabulary word in your answer. Use each word only once. Questions and answers will then contain all fifteen words (or forms of the words) from this lesson's word list.

1. What makes the Great Pyramid unusual among the places on Antipater's list?

   _____

2. How could one go from room to room within the Great Pyramid?

   _____

3. Why would the **interior** of the Great Pyramid be very dark?

   _____

4. How did the Egyptians raise the stones onto the pyramid?

   _____

5. Why did the white limestone have to come by water?

   _____

6. Why did some people work on the pyramid for only a **portion** of the year?

   _____

7. How does the room where the king's body was placed compare with other rooms?

   _____

8. Why do you think the narrative refers to the king's room as a **chamber**?

    _____

9. What are some of the **precious** objects that might have been left with the dead king?

    _____

10. Why did the Egyptians place granite slabs outside the king's tomb?

    _____

11. What happened to the gold and the jewels that were inside the tomb?

    _____

12. When (to the nearest hundred years) was the Great Pyramid built?

    _____

13. Why did the Egyptians think Cheops deserved such a magnificent tomb?

    _____

14. How does the Great Pyramid differ from when it was first built?

    _____

15. What is the **location** of Cairo?

    _____

WORDLY WISE

In Lesson 7 you learned that the Greek word for "eight" is *okto*. In Latin, it became *octo*. (An *octopus* has eight arms. *October* was the eighth month in the Roman calendar; we changed it and made it the tenth month.)

A large number of English words are formed from Greek or Latin numbers. Among them is our word **century**, a period of one hundred years. It comes from the Latin for one hundred, which is *centum*. Other words sharing this root include *cent* (There are one hundred cents in a dollar.), *centipede* (This was once thought to have one hundred legs; it actually has about seventy.), and *centimeter* (There are one hundred centimeters in a meter.).

✦ ✦ ✦ ✦ ✦ ✦

In 1976 the United States celebrated its *bicentennial*. If you knew nothing of the history of the United States, but knew that the Latin for "two" is *bi,* could you figure out how old the United States was in 1976?

How can the word **quarry** have two such separate and unrelated meanings? For the answer to this question we must look into the word's history. In fact, it is not one word but two quite different ones that by chance have the same spelling.

The word for an animal being hunted comes from the old French *cuiree,* the name for body parts fed to animals after a successful hunt. The word passed into English as *querre,* which in modern English became *quarry.*

The word for a deep pit where stone is cut out of the ground comes from the Latin *quadrum,* which means "squared at the corners." It was applied to stones used for building, which were usually squared at the corners. Later, changed over time to *quarry,* it came to mean the place from which the stone was obtained.

CROSSWORD PUZZLE

Solve the crossword puzzle below by studying the clues and filling in the answer boxes. Clues followed by a number are definitions of words in Lessons 5—8. The number gives the word list in which the answer to the clue appears.

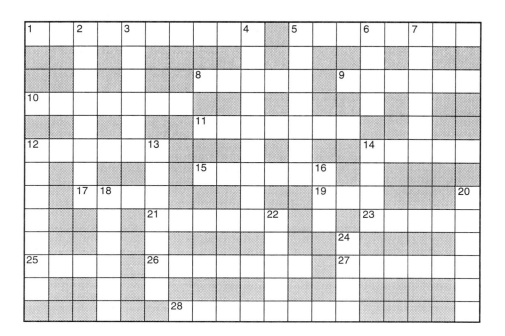

Clues Across

1. To give out (7)
5. To win over by arguing or asking (5)
8. To change in some way (7)
9. An animal that is being hunted (8)
10. The topmost part; the outer layer (8)
11. A part or share of the whole (8)
12. Twice as much
14. Each separate item on a list (8)
15. Skilled at tricking others (6)
17. Dull and without color (6)
19. Adam and _____
21. To make pure (6)
23. To take by force of the law (7)
25. Eight, _____ , ten
26. A large room (8)
27. Having nothing left out (6)
28. Place where something is (8)

Clues Down

2. To be around on all sides (7)
3. To remember (5)
4. To interest and amuse (5)
5. To go on longer than expected (5)
6. Opposite of "open"
7. Happening suddenly without warning (5)
12. To go to a lower level (8)
13. To hold closely (7)
14. Used to see with
16. Opposite of "no"
18. To say you won't accept (5)
20. Very strict or harsh
22. To throw out (7)
24. Showing a strong interest; eager (7)

Lesson 9

Word List

Study the definitions of the words below; then do the exercises for the lesson.

astonish
v. To surprise or amaze.
[It *astonished* me to find out that we were born in the same town on the same day.]
astonishment *n.* Great surprise or amazement.
[When she heard the news, her eyes opened wide in *astonishment*.]

dainty
adj. Small and fine in quality or appearance.
[These *dainty* lace handkerchiefs once belonged to my great-grandmother.]

demonstrate
v. 1. To show by doing.
[He *demonstrated* the art of juggling every weekend in the Square.]
2. To explain or prove by using examples.
[The speaker said her chart would *demonstrate* the harm that smoking does.]
3. To make a public showing of support or protest.
[A crowd gathered outside the room where the school committee was meeting to *demonstrate* in favor of the teachers.]
demonstration *n.* A showing or display of objects or feelings.
[In a *demonstration* of real courage, the firefighter ran back into the burning building to save a young child.]

devote
v. To give one's complete attention to a purpose or person.
[Florence Nightingale *devoted* her life to caring for others.]
devotion *n.* A strong love or attachment.
[Nathan Hale expressed his *devotion* to America when he said, "I only regret that I have but one life to lose for my country."]

envy
n. 1. A wish for something that someone else has.
[Her amazing soccer skill filled the team with *envy*.]
v. To wish for what someone else has.
[I *envy* my sister's skill at diving.]
envious *adj.* Filled with envy.
[Anna's best friend always does better in English than she does, but Anna is never *envious*.]

flinch
v. To move back suddenly in fear.
[I didn't even *flinch* when the dentist's drill approached my tooth.]

grieve
v. To feel deep sorrow; to be filled with sadness.
[The entire country *grieved* over the death of President Kennedy.]
grief *n.* Deep sorrow.
[People everywhere, in fact, shared the *grief* at the terrible loss.]

opponent
n. A person who is against one in a contest, game, or argument.
[We always shake hands with our *opponent* after the match.]

organize   *v.* 1. To arrange according to a system.
[The skateboard company is *organized* into three departments.]
2. To start or form.
[My father *organized* a group for single parents.]
organization   *n.* The way a group of things or people is put together or arranged; a group of people who are together for a common purpose.
[My favorite after-school *organization* is the Glee Club.]

perform   *v.* 1. To play, recite, or entertain before an audience.
[I'm too shy to *perform* my piano pieces for my relatives.]
2. To do; to carry out.
[The cleanup crew *performed* its duties cheerfully and well.]
performance   *n.* Something that is done, especially in front of an audience.
[Elvis Presley's *performance* on the Ed Sullivan show made him a star.]

propose   *v.* 1. To suggest.
[The mayor *proposed* that overnight parking be permitted in the summer.]
2. To intend.
[I *propose* to leave as soon I have completed my work.]
3. To make an offer of marriage.
[Do I have to get down on my knees when I *propose*?]
proposal   *n.* Something that is suggested.
[The architect stayed up all night working on her *proposal* for a new clinic.]

reputation   *n.* What people generally think about a person or thing.
[Abraham Lincoln had a *reputation* for honesty.]

resent   *v.* To feel anger or annoyance at.
[I *resent* the special treatment my brother always gets.]
resentful   *adj.* Feeling angry or annoyed.
[When I have to do all the cleanup by myself I get *resentful*.]
resentment   *n.* A feeling of anger or annoyance.
[Nick couldn't hide his *resentment* at having to miss recess.]

scarce   *adj.* In short supply; not plentiful.
[Gasoline was *scarce* during World War II.]

surplus   *n.* The amount that is more than is needed.
[Abdul filled the flower pots with soil and stored the *surplus* in the shed.]
adj. More than is needed.
[I have quite a big garden, so I always have *surplus* zucchini.]

9A Finding Meanings

Choose two phrases to form a sentence that correctly uses a word from Word List 9. Write each sentence in the space provided.

1. (a) A company's proposal is
   (b) the amount it is worth.

   (c) A company's reputation is
   (d) the general view that people have of it.

2. (a) something that is begun.
   (b) an extra amount.
   (c) A surplus is
   (d) A performance is

3. (a) who is highly skilled.
   (b) A dainty thing is one
   (c) that is small and finely made.
   (d) A resentful person is one

4. (a) a show put on before an audience.
   (b) A performance is
   (c) Astonishment is
   (d) a shrinking back in fear.

5. (a) a feeling of anger.
   (b) deep sorrow.
   (c) Resentment is
   (d) Organization is

6. (a) suffer in silence.
   (b) To envy is to
   (c) To flinch is to
   (d) shrink back in fear.

7. (a) a public showing of something.
   (b) A demonstration of something is
   (c) the complete absence of something.
   (d) An opponent of something is

8. (a) To envy someone is
   (b) To astonish someone is
   (c) to want what that person has.
   (d) to be afraid of that person.

9. (a) To organize is to
   (b) be filled with sadness.
   (c) To grieve is to
   (d) scatter in all directions.

10. (a) A proposal is
    (b) a suggestion.
    (c) An opponent is
    (d) a show put on before an audience.

9B Just the Right Word

Improve each of the following sentences by crossing out the italicized phrase and replacing it with a word (or a form of the word) from Word List 9.

1. Because of last week's storm, fish will be *in very short supply* for a while.

2. I *feel anger and annoyance over* the fact that these extra costs were not disclosed when I signed the contract.

3. The cast was not used to *putting on a show* on such a small stage.

4. The two *persons who were playing against each other* waited for the umpire to signal the start of the tennis match.

5. City workers *gathered to make a public protest* against further wage cuts.

6. Ben was *filled with surprise* when he won the spelling contest.

7. Susan B. Anthony was *willing to give all her time and energy* to the cause of women's rights.

8. The success of your business ventures fills me with *longing for what you have achieved.*

9. Can anyone join this new neighborhood *group of people who have come together for a common purpose?*

10. The first time my father *made an offer of marriage* to my mother, she turned him down.

9C Applying Meanings

Circle the letter of each correct answer to the questions below. A question may have more than one correct answer.

1. Which of the following might *astonish* you?
   (a) a flying chicken   (c) a ten-pound pumpkin
   (b) a barking cat   (d) a ten-pound tomato

2. Which of the following might be called *dainty?*
   (a) a thin china teacup   (c) a pair of ballet slippers
   (b) a pair of size-12 boots   (d) a thick coffee mug

3. Which of the following might make a person *flinch?*
   (a) a scary scene in a movie   (c) a round of applause
   (b) a large rock falling nearby   (d) a clap of thunder

4. Which of the following might cause *grief?*
   (a) being rejected by one's friends (c) losing a pet cat
   (b) losing all one's money   (d) winning a prize

5. Which of the following could be *organized?*
   (a) a party   (c) the weather
   (b) one's personal papers   (d) a club

6. In which of the following would someone have an *opponent?*
   (a) a boxing match   (c) a writing class
   (b) a chess game   (d) a walk on the beach

7. Which of the following could a person *perform?*
   (a) a change in the weather   (c) a part in a play
   (b) a card trick   (d) a piece of music

8. Which of the following might make a person *resentful?*
   (a) being praised   (c) being mocked
   (b) being ignored   (d) being grounded

9D Completing the Thought

Read each sentence below and fill in the blank with the correct word (or a form of the word) from the word list.

1. None of his friends knew whether or not to believe Zachary's story, since he was famous for his tall tales. His _____ was well-known.

2. A few of Mark's classmates made fun of him for doing well on the English test. Maybe they were _____.

3. Because of the approaching hurricane, everyone rushed out to buy candles; by late afternoon it was impossible to find any in the local stores. Candles were becoming very, very, _____.

4. A reporter for the *Globe* asked the school board chair if there were any plans for dealing with the budget cuts. She wanted to know what the school board _____ to do.

| demonstrate |
| devote |
| envy |
| organize |
| perform |
| propose |
| reputation |
| resent |
| scarce |
| surplus |

5. The tests on the new engine were a great success. The engine _____ better than expected.

6. The twenty people who signed up with Nala when she offered to arrange a trip to Puerto Rico were very pleased with their travels. They said Nala was a very good _____.

7. On her first television cooking show, Alicia gave a lesson on sharpening and caring for kitchen knives. It was a very useful _____.

8. George Washington's feelings for his country were shown clearly by his actions, and no one ever questioned them. There was no doubt of his _____.

9. The Fallowes had grown far more corn than they needed for their own family, so they decided to share what they didn't need. They offered their neighbors the _____.

10. Muadi had such a calm and cheerful personality that it didn't even bother him when people teased him about his accent. He never seemed _____.

9E Narrative   *Read the narrative below, then complete the exercise that follows.*

ANNIE OAKLEY

In the late 1800s, people all over the world thrilled to the excitement of Buffalo Bill's Wild West Show. Its greatest star was Annie Oakley, a young woman who entertained millions with her sharpshooting skills. She could shoot a hole in a dime tossed in the air. She could hit the thin edge of a playing card at thirty paces. She could even hit a target while riding backward on a horse that was galloping around the ring.

Annie Oakley's real name was Phoebe Anne Oakley Mozee. She grew up in Ohio, just after the Civil War. Her mother was a widow with a large family. Food was **scarce**, and Annie helped to feed the family by trapping quail. One day she decided to try shooting them instead. She quickly became such an expert shot that she hardly ever missed. Soon her family had more birds than they could eat, and Annie sold the **surplus** to local store owners. She was then nine years old.

At first people found it hard to believe that Annie could be so good with a rifle because she seemed to be such a **dainty** person. But when she was fifteen, she entered a shooting contest. Her **opponent** was a man named Frank Butler. He had the **reputation** of being the best shot in the county, and the contest was **organized** to find out whether or not Annie could beat him. It gave her the chance to **demonstrate** just how good she really was. Frank hit the target twenty-four times and missed only on his last shot. The people watching were impressed, but they were **astonished** when Annie hit the target twenty-five times in a row.

Frank Butler was so impressed that he invited Annie to join his sharpshooting act. He became so fond of her that he **proposed** marriage, and they were married when she was sixteen. She adopted the stage name Annie Oakley, and she and Frank **performed** together in circuses and stage shows as Butler and Oakley. In one part of their act, Frank would stand still while Annie, from across the stage, shot a cigarette out of his mouth. Frank never **flinched,** and Annie never missed.

They joined Buffalo Bill's Wild West Show in 1885, and stayed with it for seventeen years. Annie Oakley became famous all over the world, but Frank was never **envious** of his wife's skill and did not **resent** her success. They were **devoted** to each other and lived together happily for almost fifty years. When Annie died in 1926, Frank could not **grieve** long. He died just three weeks later.

Answer each of the following questions in a sentence. If a question does not contain a vocabulary word, use a vocabulary word in your answer. Use each word only once. Questions and answers will then contain all fifteen words (or forms of the words) from this lesson's word list.

1. How does the narrative make clear that Annie Oakley and Frank Butler loved each other very much?

   _____

2. Where did Annie first meet Frank Butler?

   _____

3. Why was the shooting match arranged?

   _____

4. Why was the shooting contest between Oakley and Butler of so much interest?

   _____

5. How can you tell that Annie Oakley and Frank Butler were probably rarely apart?

   _____

6. Why might her husband have **envied** Annie Oakley's success?

   _____

7. Why is it obvious that Frank Butler didn't **resent** Annie's beating him in the shooting contest?

   _____

8. What is the meaning of **proposed** as it is used in the narrative?

_____

9. Why did Annie seem an unlikely person to win a shooting contest?

_____

10. Why did Annie start trapping quail?

_____

11. How did Annie earn money when she was nine?

_____

12. How did Annie Oakley **demonstrate** her skill?

_____

13. What do you think was the most **astonishing** trick that Annie could do?

_____

14. Why do you think Frank didn't **flinch** when Annie shot a cigarette out of his mouth?

_____

15. Did Frank **grieve** very long after Annie's death?

_____

WORDLY WISE

A synonym for *astounded,* which you learned in Lesson 4, is **astonished.** A third synonym, *thunderstruck,* is less common and suggests a much greater degree of surprise. Both *astound* and *astonish* are formed from the Latin verb *tonare,* which means "to thunder."

The word **opponent** is formed from the Latin prefix *ob-,* which means "against," together with the root from the Latin verb *ponere,* which means "to place." Your *opponent* in a contest or competition is the person who is *placed* there and is *against* you.

Lesson 10

Word List

Study the definitions of the words below; then do the exercises for the lesson.

ail
v. To cause sickness, pain, or trouble.
["What *ails* you?" the doctor asked.]
ailment *n.* An illness; a disease.
[Measles is a common childhood *ailment*.]
ailing *adj.* In poor health.
[I have been *ailing* all winter.]

banish
v. 1. To force someone out of the country.
[When the tsars ruled Russia, lawbreakers were *banished* to Siberia.]
2. To get rid of completely.
[Joe was such a cheerful person, he *banished* gloom wherever he went.]

communicate
v. To make known; to give or exchange information.
[Since I hate to write letters, we *communicate* mostly by telephone.]
communication *n.* The exchange of information between people.
[The misunderstanding was caused by a lack of *communication* between us.]
communicative *adj.* Willing to speak; eager to talk.
[When I asked her where she had been, she was not very *communicative,* replying only, "Out."]

console
v. To make less sad; to comfort.
[My parents tried to *console* me when my best friend moved away.]
consolation *n.* Comfort.
[I knew I could always turn to my aunt for *consolation* whenever I was upset.]

cower
v. To shrink from, as if from fear.
[When I saw the poor dog *cower*, I knew its master was cruel.]

deliberate
adj. (duh ′lib er ut) Carefully thought out; not hasty.
[Although my mother was angry, she spoke in a calm and *deliberate* manner.]
v. (duh ′lib er āte) To think carefully in order to make up one's mind.
[We *deliberated* a long time before deciding to move to Arizona.]

depth
n. Distance from top to bottom or front to back; deepness.
[The floodwaters reached a *depth* of several feet.]
depths *n. pl.* The innermost part or the deepest part.
[The treasure chest lay buried in the *depths* of the sea.]

desire
v. To wish for; to want very much.
[A person who is famished *desires* just one thing—food!]
n. A strong wish.
[Pizarro's *desire* for gold was so great he ordered the Inca king, Atahualpa, to fill three rooms with it.
desirable *adj.* Pleasing, agreeable.
[My new school is in a very *desirable* location.]

livelihood
n. The means of supporting oneself.
[The storekeepers in Key West depend on tourists for their *livelihood*.]

misfortune   *n.* 1. Bad luck; trouble.
[He had the *misfortune* to break his leg right before the big game.]
2. An unlucky event.
[The 1992 hurricane was Florida's worst *misfortune* in many years.]

orphan   *n.* A child whose parents are dead.
[Tom Sawyer lived with his Aunt Polly because he was an *orphan*.]

precipice   *n.* A very high and steep cliff.
[We stood watchfully on the edge of the *precipice* and looked down.]
precipitous   *adj.* 1. Very steep.
[The Two-Mile Terror ski trail has many *precipitous* slopes.]
2. Hasty; abrupt; done without careful thought.
[Joining the navy so suddenly was a *precipitous* act.]

regain   *v.* To get back.
[By following the doctor's orders, I slowly *regained* my health.]

slay   *v.* To kill violently. (*slain,* past participle)
[The scene where Saint George *slays* the dragon comes right at the end of the play.]

symptom   *n.* A sign of something.
[Headaches can be a *symptom* of eyestrain.]

10A Finding Meanings

Choose two phrases to form a sentence that correctly uses a word from Word List 10. Write each sentence in the space provided.

1. (a) To slay someone is to   (c) send that person away.
   (b) To banish someone is to   (d) tell that person something.

2. (a) One's misfortune is   (c) the way one makes a living.
   (b) the way one treats other people.   (d) One's livelihood is

3. (a) A precipitous drop in price is   (c) A desirable drop in price is
   (b) one that is big and unexpected.   (d) one that is very small.

4. (a) To communicate something is to   (c) decide not to take it.
   (b) get it back.   (d) To regain something is to

5. (a) to be loved.   (c) To be ailing is
   (b) to be ill.   (d) To be deliberate is

6. (a) Consolation is   (c) the giving of information.
   (b) Communication is   (d) a series of unlucky events.

7. (a) A deliberate change   (c) is one that is agreeable.
   (b) A desirable change   (d) is one that is hardly noticed.

8. (a) To slay someone is to   (c) To console someone is to
   (b) comfort that person.   (d) envy that person.

9. (a) a large sum of money.   (c) the distance from top to bottom.
   (b) Depth is   (d) Misfortune is

10. (a) a close family member.   (c) A symptom is
    (b) a sign of something.   (d) An orphan is

10B Just the Right Word

Improve each of the following sentences by crossing out the italicized phrase and replacing it with a word (or a form of the word) from Word List 10.

1. The judges *gave a great deal of thought and talked among themselves* for a long time before announcing the winner of the science fair.

2. The worst *bad luck* to hit the town was the closing of the shipyard.

3. Hunters who *violently kill* baby seals for their fur will be stopped.

4. "You don't look well. What *is the matter with* you?" asked Jorge.

5. He expressed a *strong wish* to spend more time with his children.

6. It took the climbers an hour to descend the *steep cliff that went straight down.*

7. We used to *shrink back in fear* whenever we heard her voice.

8. When Luisa's pet rabbit died, she began writing in her journal every night for *something to give her comfort.*

9. The *children whose parents had been killed* were all adopted by families in town.

10. If you want this venture to succeed, you must *get rid of* any thoughts of failure.

11. I was moved to the *very deepest parts* of my soul by the sight of the northern lights flashing across the sky.

10C Applying Meanings

Circle the letter of each correct answer to the questions below. A question may have more than one correct answer.

1. Which of the following can have *depth?*
   - (a) a drawer
   - (b) a pond
   - (c) a point
   - (d) a shelf

2. Which of the following might an actor *desire?*
   - (a) perfect teeth
   - (b) applause
   - (c) decayed teeth
   - (d) a good role

3. Which of the following is a way to *communicate?*
   - (a) watching television
   - (b) talking on the phone
   - (c) reading a book
   - (d) writing a letter

4. Which of the following is an *ailment?*
   - (a) measles
   - (b) anger
   - (c) baldness
   - (d) hunger

5. Which of the following might be a person's *livelihood?*
   - (a) attending school
   - (b) mowing lawns
   - (c) washing cars
   - (d) taking out the trash

6. Which of the following might be a *deliberate* act?
   - (a) stumbling
   - (b) singing
   - (c) lying
   - (d) sneezing

7. Which of the following could be *precipitous?*
   - (a) a fall in price
   - (b) an action
   - (c) a cliff
   - (d) a road

8. Which of the following could be *regained*?
   (a) one's past
   (c) one's health
   (b) one's reputation
   (d) one's memory

10D Completing the Thought

Read each sentence below and fill in the blank with the correct word (or a form of the word) from the word list.

1. When both his parents were killed in a plane crash, Dimitri went to live with his Aunt Lucy, his mother's sister, who lived in Yonkers. Dimitri was an _____.

2. When her mother asked Louisa why she needed the extra money, she didn't answer. When her mother pressed her, Louisa just shrugged and said, "I have to go now." Louisa was not very _____.

3. First Josh missed the bus, then he missed the train, then when he finally got on, there were no seats. His day was a series of _____.

| ailment |
| communicate |
| cower |
| depth |
| misfortune |
| orphan |
| regain |
| slay |
| symptom |

4. When the twins both broke out in spots and started scratching, their mother was sure that they had caught the chicken pox. She could tell by their _____.

5. After scoring first, the Twins allowed the Tigers to get on top with a three-run homer in the seventh, but the Twins won in the end by a score of 7-4. The Twins _____ the lead.

6. German measles is not usually serious in children, and most young people get it at some time. It is a common childhood _____.

7. Allison measured the shelf and decided that it was too narrow to hold the large boxes she wanted to put on it. It didn't have enough _____.

8. Before Moustapha studied public speaking, he used to be terrified of being called on by the teacher. It's been a long time since he _____ in fear in the back of the room.

9. The battle of Gettysburg resulted in a victory for the North, but it wasn't a victory without great cost. Tens of thousands were _____.

10E Narrative

Read the narrative below; then complete the exercise that follows.

TOKOYO AND THE SEA MONSTER

Folktales are stories passed on from adults to children without ever being written down. Every country has its folktales, and this one comes from Japan. It is the story of a young pearl diver named Tokoyo.

The people of Tokoyo's village made their **livelihood** diving for pearls. Tokoyo was the youngest of the divers. She could stay underwater longer and collect more oysters than anyone, searching for the one oyster in a thousand that contained a precious pearl. The sea was like a second home to her, and she swam easily through its **depths,** cutting oysters from the rocks with her razor-sharp pearling knife.

The other pearl divers were all the family Tokoyo had. Her mother had died when she was a baby, and while she was still a child **misfortune** struck again. Her father, whose sense of humor had gotten him into trouble before, had made a joke about the fact that the emperor was always sick. Because making fun of the emperor was a crime, Tokoyo's father was **banished** to the island of Oki, far from the Japanese mainland. To make matters worse, **communication** between Tokoyo and her father was forbidden. Her friends tried to **console** the young girl, but they could not lift her spirits. She felt like an **orphan,** and the house that had once been filled with laughter was now filled with sorrow.

Tokoyo's one **desire** was to see her father. On her fifteenth birthday, she left her village and set off for Oki. Soon after landing on the island, Tokoyo saw a group of people standing on the edge of a cliff with a girl about her own age who was dressed all in white. People explained to Tokoyo that the evil sea god that made its home in the waters off the island demanded the life of a young girl once a year. They told her that the girl **cowering** before them had been chosen as the sea god's victim and was about to be thrown into the sea. Then they said that the sea god had also cast a spell on the emperor, causing his many **ailments.** When she heard this, Tokoyo saw a chance to help her father. She begged people to let her take the girl's place. They began to **deliberate** among themselves while Tokoyo waited anxiously. Finally, to her great relief, they agreed.

Tokoyo walked to the edge of the **precipice,** took a deep breath, and leaped into the water. She swam deeper and deeper until, at the bottom of the sea, she found herself face to face with the evil sea god. Tokoyo drew her pearling knife, **slaying** the evil sea god and thus ending the spell he had cast on the emperor. In an instant, all the emperor's **symptoms** disappeared. He was delighted to be rid of the doctors who had attended him, and when he learned of Tokoyo's brave deed, he promised the young girl whatever she wanted. As a result of Tokoyo's wish, her father **regained** his freedom and was happily reunited with his daughter.

Answer each of the following questions in a sentence. If a question does not contain a vocabulary word, use a vocabulary word in your answer. Use each word only once. Questions and answers will then contain all fifteen words (or forms of the words) from this lesson's word list.

1. Explain why the story of Tokoyo and the evil sea god has a happy ending?

   _____

2. Was Tokoyo an **orphan**?

   _____

3. What does "**misfortune** struck" mean as it is used in the narrative?

   _____

4. Why did the emperor need doctors?

   _____

5. How does the narrative make clear that Tokoyo's friends were kind to her?

   _____

6. Where did the evil sea god live?

   _____

7. Explain why Tokoyo's fight with the sea god was a **deliberate** act.

   _____

8. Why didn't Tokoyo's father write to her?

   _____

9. Why was Tokoyo's father living on the island of Oki?

   _____

10. Why did Tokoyo go to the island of Oki?

    _____

11. Why had the girl in white been taken to the **precipice**?

    _____

12. How can you tell that the girl in white was afraid?

_____

13. Why did Tokoyo want to take the girl's place?

_____

14. How did the emperor know that the spell had been broken?

_____

15. Why did the people of Tokoyo's village dive for oysters?

_____

WORDLY WISE

One of the world's oldest languages is Sanskrit. It was spoken in India thousands of years ago and is the special language of the Hindu religion. Very few people speak it today, but some words in European languages are connected to Sanskrit. **Orphan** is one of them. An *orphan* is a child without parents who therefore can be in a weak and helpless state. The word comes from the Sanskrit *arbha,* which means "weak; helpless."

Lesson 11

Word List
Study the definitions of the words below; then do the exercises for the lesson.

annual
adj. Happening every year.
[Somerville's *annual* town meeting is in March.]
n. 1. A plant that lives for one year.
[Impatiens is my favorite *annual*.]
2. A book that comes out once a year.
[I save all my NFL football *annuals*.]

artificial
adj. Made by human beings and not by nature.
[My Aunt Rosa says she can taste the difference between *artificial* sweeteners and real sugar.]

blend
v. 1. To come or mix together into one.
[Make sure you *blend* the butter and sugar before you add the flour.]
2. To go together.
[The painter chose colors that *blend* well.]
n. A mixture.
[Mocha is a *blend* of chocolate and coffee.]

bore
v. 1. To make a round hole in by drilling.
[If you *bore* a hole in the wood first, you won't split it when you put in the screw.]
2. To tire by being dull and uninteresting.
[The yawns of my listeners told me I was beginning to *bore* them.]
n. A dull and uninteresting person.
[He tells that same joke so often that he is becoming a terrible *bore*.]
boring *adj.* Dull and uninteresting.
[She sometimes stretches the facts a little, but her stories are never *boring*.]
boredom *n.* A state of being bored.
[When heads began to nod and eyes to close, you could tell *boredom* had set in.]

considerable
adj. Great; large.
[Although my grandmother's house is a *considerable* distance from town, she walks to the post office there every day.]

crude
adj. 1. Raw; in an unrefined state.
[Refineries turn *crude* oil into gasoline.]
2. Roughly made.
[Andrea drew me a *crude* map with a crayon on a scrap of paper.]
3. Ill-mannered.
[As we walked back from school, we tried to ignore their *crude* remarks.]

evaporate
v. 1. To change from water into steam or vapor.
[The water in the kettle boiled so long that it all *evaporated*.]
2. To disappear.
[By the third day on the mountain, our hopes of being rescued began to *evaporate*.]

foliage
n. The leaves of trees and other plants.
[The house at the end of the road was completely hidden by *foliage*.]

gash   *n.* A long, deep cut.
[When Liza slipped on the rocks, she had to go to the hospital to have the *gash* in her leg sewn up.]

hue   *n.* A color; especially a shade of color.
[The poppies in Monet's paintings stand out because of their vivid reddish-orange *hues*.]

increase   *v.* To make or become larger; to add to.
[I'm going to ask my mother to *increase* my allowance on my next birthday.]
n. The amount by which something gets larger.
[A wet spring usually means an *increase* in the number of mosquitoes.]

nourish   *v.* To feed; to support or make grow.
[We *nourish* our bodies best by eating a diet of fruits, vegetables, and grains.]
nourishment   *n.* Anything that feeds or helps to make grow.
[When I had the flu, the only *nourishment* I could take was clear chicken broth.]

vary   *v.* To make or have a change in.
[The length of a calendar month *varies* between twenty-eight and thirty-one days.]
variation   *n.* A change in form, position, or condition.
[There isn't much *variation* between the summer and the winter temperatures where my grandfather lives.]

vision   *n.* 1. Eyesight.
[If you are lucky enough to have 20/20 *vision*, you'll be able to see well.]
2. Something seen in the mind, especially of the future.
[The founders of the United Nations had a *vision* of a world without hunger or war.]
visual   *adj.* Of or used in seeing.
[Actually seeing the osprey gave us *visual* proof that they were still alive.]

yield   *v.* 1. To give up someone or something; to surrender.
[Congress finally *yielded* to the president's demands and passed the budget.]
2. To produce.
[Twenty gallons of milk will *yield* about one pound of butter.]
n. The amount produced.
[The farmer told us that you can expect a *yield* of about fifty pounds of fruit from each apple tree.]

11A Finding Meanings

Choose two phrases to form a sentence that correctly uses a word from Word List 11. Write each sentence in the space provided.

1. (a) one that is quite large.
   (b) A considerable amount is
   (c) An increased amount is
   (d) one that is reduced.

---

2. (a) is not fully developed.
   (b) An artificial aid is one that
   (c) A visual aid is one that
   (d) helps one to see.

3. (a) A blend is
   (b) a long, deep cut.
   (c) A bore is
   (d) a dull and uninteresting person.

4. (a) A gash is
   (b) a round hole made by a drill.
   (c) something that appears once a year.
   (d) An annual is

5. (a) To increase is
   (b) to be mixed together.
   (c) to grow.
   (d) To evaporate is

6. (a) Crude rubber is
   (b) Artificial rubber is
   (c) still in a raw state.
   (d) a mixture of different kinds.

7. (a) Colors that blend are those that
   (b) go well together.
   (c) quickly fade.
   (d) Colors that vary are those that

8. (a) A gash is
   (b) a deep cut.
   (c) a careless remark.
   (d) A hue is

9. (a) to give way.
   (b) To yield is
   (c) To evaporate is
   (d) to melt.

10. (a) the wood that comes from it.
    (b) A tree's foliage is
    (c) its leaves.
    (d) A tree's hue is

11. (a) Something that nourishes
    (b) Something that varies
    (c) does not stay the same.
    (d) keeps getting smaller.

11B Just the Right Word

Improve each of the following sentences by crossing out the italicized phrase and replacing it with a word (or a form of the word) from Word List 11.

1. The *amount produced* from these oil wells is a thousand barrels a day.

2. Basil is a(n) *plant that grows for just one season.*

3. Mr. Martinez loves to talk about his new computer, but he can get very *dull and uninteresting.*

4. Spilled gasoline *turns to vapor* and mixes with the air quickly.

5. Manure *provides food for* growing plants.

6. The *roughly made* drawing was the work of a very young child.

7. Julio's favorite sandwich filling is made by *mixing together* peanut butter and honey.

8. These interior paints come in many different *shades of color.*

9. Isabel is a person whose *sense of the future* of the city's parks will be appealing to both young and old.

10. The flowers on the piano look so real that you cannot tell they are *made by human hands.*

11C Applying Meanings

Circle the letter of each correct answer to the questions below. A question may have more than one correct answer.

1. Which of the following might *evaporate?*
   (a) coal
   (b) water
   (c) gasoline
   (d) electricity

2. Which of the following is an *increase?*
   (a) from Maine to Mexico
   (b) from A to Z
   (c) from 18 to 18
   (d) from several to many

3. Which of the following is a *considerable* amount?
   (a) ten cents
   (b) a thousand dollars
   (c) fifty tons
   (d) a modest sum

4. Which of the following have *foliage?*
   (a) rose bushes
   (b) apple trees
   (c) cactus plants
   (d) garden vegetables

5. Which of the following could cause a *gash?*
   (a) a sharp rock
   (b) a baseball
   (c) a hammer
   (d) an ax

6. Which of the following is a *hue?*
   (a) pink
   (b) yellow
   (c) black
   (d) white

7. For which of the following would you need your *vision?*
   (a) making sure your socks match
   (b) observing Thanksgiving
   (c) listening to the radio
   (d) observing the moon

8. Which of the following would a seven-year-old probably find *boring?*
   (a) a visit to a circus
   (b) a ride on a roller coaster
   (c) a speech by a state senator
   (d) a TV discussion of proper diet

11D Completing the Thought

Read each sentence below and fill in the blank with the correct word (or a form of the word) from the word list.

1. The Essex county fair is held every September and draws people from all over New England. It is an _____ event.

2. The owners of the new baseball stadium decided to get rid of the Astroturf. The players complained that it felt too _____.

3. When she prepared an Indian meal, Sarina made up a curry powder containing cayenne, turmeric, cumin, and other spices. Curry powder is a _____ of different spices.

4. Salvador is fun to be with because he finds everything interesting. He never suffers from _____.

5. When they were little, the twins talked with their mouths full, dropped food on the floor, and didn't wash their hands before coming to the table. They had _____ table manners.

annual
artificial
blend
bore
crude
increase
nourish
vary
yield

6. When her mother took Stella into the clinic for her six-month check-up, she learned that the baby had grown two inches and had gained twelve pounds. She was really pleased at the _____.

7. Candy bars may taste good, but they are not as good for you as fruits, vegetables, and cereals. There is not much _____ in candy bars.

8. The wallpaper was all supposed to be from the same lot, but you will notice this roll is a bit lighter than some of the first ones we put up. There is some _____ in the rolls.

9. The Gallaghers collect about a hundred pounds of honey from their ten hives. They are very satisfied with this _____.

11E Narrative

Read the narrative below; then complete the exercise that follows.

MAPLE SUGARING

In the late fall, one of nature's most magnificent sights is the **foliage** of New England's maple trees, blazing with color. The many **hues** range from the fiery reds of the swamp maples to the rich golds of the sugar maples.

In the spring, though, some trees offer more than just a **visual** treat. Early in the season, buckets dangle from the sides of sugar maples, collecting sap for the **annual** maple sugaring.

The amount of sap that can be collected from a healthy tree **varies** between twelve and twenty gallons, which will **yield** from two to four pounds of maple syrup. This will leave plenty of sap for the tree to **nourish** itself as it enters a new growing season.

The weather has a great deal to do with how much sap a tree produces. The flow is greatest when the days are sunny and the nights are cold. The flow of sap slows down at night and **increases** during the day. Maple trees in low, wet areas produce more sap than trees growing in higher and drier parts, but the sap contains less sugar.

Native Americans showed the first settlers how to make maple syrup. They used to make **gashes** in the trees with axes in order to let the sap run out, but this could cause **considerable** damage to the tree. Today, tree farmers **bore** a small hole into each tree, about three feet above the ground, and this does no harm.

When it trickles from the tree, the syrup is in **crude** form; it needs to be refined before it is ready to use. It is boiled in large kettles until the water **evaporates**. The syrup that remains is passed through filters to clean it. It is then ready to be poured on waffles and pancakes or made into the maple sugar candy so popular with visitors to New England.

Maple syrup is produced only in North America in a season that lasts four to six weeks. Besides New England, maple sugaring is carried out in several other northern states, as well as the Canadian provinces of Quebec and Ontario. Much of the syrup that Americans pour on their pancakes is not real maple syrup, however. It is made from cane sugar syrup with **artificial** maple flavoring added. The makers may **blend** it with real maple syrup so that the label can say "Contains Real Maple Syrup." One hundred percent maple syrup costs more, but those who enjoy its taste say that there is nothing like the real thing.

Answer each of the following questions in a sentence. If a question does not contain a vocabulary word, use a vocabulary word in your answer. Use each word only once. Questions and answers will then contain all fifteen words (or forms of the words) from this lesson's word list.

1. What do the words "Contains Real Maple Syrup" on the label tell you?

   _____

2. Why do you think **artificial** maple syrup costs less than the real thing?

   _____

3. What is another word for the leaves of a tree?

   _____

4. In what season do maple trees become a **visual** treat?

   _____

5. If you were hiking in New England in the fall, what **hues** might you see?

   _____

6. How much sap can be collected from a sugar maple?

   _____

7. What is the meaning of **yield** as it is used in the narrative?

   _____

8. Why do trees produce sap?

   _____

9. Why do you think people gathering sap prefer sunny days?

_____

10. Why did the first settlers need axes to get at the sap?

_____

11. Why don't people use this method any more?

_____

12. Explain why you might see small round holes in the trunks of sugar maples.

_____

13. Why don't people use the syrup that collects in the buckets immediately?

_____

14. What happens when sap is boiled?

_____

15 How often does maple sugaring occur?

_____

WORDLY WISE

Homonyms are words that sound alike but have different meanings; they may or may not be spelled differently. **Bore** and *boar* (a male pig) are homonyms.

Crude and *refined* are antonyms. (*Crude* sugar is purified by boiling and filtering; it then becomes *refined* sugar.)

Another word for steam is *vapor*. It comes unchanged from the Latin word *vapor*, which means "steam." The Latin prefix *ex-* means "out;" before certain letters, *ex-* is shortened to *e-*. This happens with the word **evaporate**. When water *e-vapor-ates* by being warmed, the water in the form of steam, or *vapor*, is drawn *out* into the air.

Lesson 12

Word List

Study the definitions of the words below; then do the exercises for the lesson.

ability   *n.* Power or knowledge; skill.
[Lani's *ability* to do math problems in her head astounded her teacher.]

amiable   *adj.* Friendly; good natured and pleasant.
[My uncle's *amiable* manner put my friends at ease right away.]

bliss   *n.* Complete joy or happiness.
[My idea of *bliss* is an afternoon on the river with my fishing rod.]
blissful   *adj.* Very happy; joyful.
[The proud parents wore *blissful* smiles as they watched their son graduate.]

caress   *v.* To touch in a tender or loving way.
[Sean *caressed* the baby's forehead gently as it lay sleeping.]
n. A tender or loving touch or hug.
[In the nineteenth century a couple who were going to marry could not exchange a *caress* in public.]

clutch   *v.* To grasp or hold tightly to.
[Kabir *clutched* his teddy bear as he climbed into the dentist's chair.]
n. The part of a machine that connects and disconnects the power from the rest of the machine.
[Before changing gears in a standard shift car, first step on the *clutch*.]

coax   *v.* To persuade or urge in a gentle way.
[I *coaxed* my baby sister into holding my hand as we crossed the street.]

furious   *adj.* 1. Very, very angry.
[The emperor was *furious* when he realized how the two "tailors" had tricked him.]
2. Very fast, strong, or wild.
[I was confused by the *furious* activity going on in the kitchen.]
fury   *n.* 1. Great anger.
[Fern turned on her father with *fury*: "Don't hurt Wilbur," she yelled.]
2. Wild and uncontrolled force.
[The *fury* of the storm was far greater than had been forecast.]

gesture   *n.* 1. A movement of the arm or hand.
[The president waved his arm in a farewell *gesture* before boarding Air Force One.]
2. Something done to show one's feelings.
[Asking you to the birthday party was Dolores's *gesture* of friendship.]
v. To make a movement of the arm or hand.
[The coach *gestured* to the players on the bench to join her on the field.]

mope   *v.* To be sad and gloomy; to lose interest in the things that usually bring pleasure.
[As the long, hot summer days went on and I still had no job, I began to *mope*.]

| prefer | *v.* To like better; to choose first.
[Which do you *prefer*, chocolate or vanilla?]
preference *n.* That which is preferred.
[If you don't have a *preference*, I'll choose the movie.] |
|---|---|
| recover | *v.* 1. To get back to a normal state; to get well again.
[Patrizia soon *recovered* from the flu.]
2. To get back what was lost or stolen.
[It cost a hundred dollars to *recover* my car after it was towed.]
recovery *n.* 1. A return to a normal state.
[Dr. Holberg was surprised at the speed of my *recovery*.]
2. The act of getting back what was lost or stolen.
[The museum is offering a reward for the *recovery* of the missing painting.] |
| replace | *v.* 1. To take the place of.
[Who will *replace* Mr. Myers when he leaves the school?]
2. To put back in place.
[When you are through with the encyclopedias, let the librarian *replace* them on the shelves.]
replacement *n.* A person or thing that takes the place of another.
[If the water pump cannot be repaired, the plumber will order a *replacement* for us.] |
| request | *v.* To ask for.
[I *requested* a chocolate cake with cherry frosting for my birthday.]
n. The thing asked for.
[The band leader agreed to play our *request*.] |
| separate | *v.* To set or keep apart.
[Whenever the twins start fighting, my mother *separates* them.]
adj. Not together; not joined.
[The twins asked if they could have *separate* bedrooms.] |
| shun | *v.* To take special pains to avoid; to keep away from.
[Most fifth graders will *shun* someone who is mean to small children.] |

12A Finding Meanings

Choose two phrases to form a sentence that correctly uses a word from Word List 12. Write each sentence in the space provided.

1. (a) To shun something
   (b) To recover something
   (c) is to want it very badly.
   (d) is to have nothing to do with it.

_____

2. (a) To be amiable is to be
   (b) very angry.
   (c) talkative.
   (d) To be furious is to be

_____

3. (a) To separate people is to   (c) try to persuade them to do something.
    (b) make them angry.   (d) To coax people is to

4. (a) To prefer something is   (c) To recover something is
    (b) to get it back.   (d) to get closer to it.

5. (a) A caress is   (c) a warm and loving touch.
    (b) A request is   (d) a warning of possible danger.

6. (a) To clutch something is to   (c) To prefer something is to
    (b) like it better than something else.   (d) let go of it.

7. (a) To separate something is to   (c) To request something is to
    (b) ask for it.   (d) hold tightly to it.

8. (a) A gesture is   (c) someone who takes the place of another.
    (b) A replacement is   (d) something said as a joke.

9. (a) great anger.   (c) Bliss is
    (b) deep sadness.   (d) Fury is

10. (a) A clutch is   (c) a warning not to get any closer.
    (b) A gesture is   (d) a movement of the arm or hand.

12B Just the Right Word

Improve each of the following sentences by crossing out the italicized phrase and replacing it with a word (or a form of the word) from Word List 12.

1. Andrea and Lucia have to be *kept apart* because they giggle so much if they sit together.

2. I *made a movement of my arm* to draw attention to the car I was interested in driving.

3. I had just one *thing I wanted to ask for*, and that was a large glass of cold lemonade.

4. Irina had the chicken pox, but made a quick *return to good health*.

5. Angela *lost interest in the things that usually gave her pleasure* for weeks after Julio moved away.

6. Our old car needs a new *part that connects and disconnects power from the engine*.

7. Around 1900 the automobile began to *take the place of* the horse and buggy.

8. My *having knowledge of how* to speak Spanish was what got me the job in the court.

9. The runners set off at a *very fast* pace.

10. A look of *complete happiness* crossed Mai-Ying's face when she heard that she had won the scholarship.

12C Applying Meanings

Circle the letter of each correct answer to the questions below. A question may have more than one correct answer.

1. Which of the following would an *amiable* person do?
   (a) avoid other people   (c) get angry easily
   (b) greet you with a smile (d) make friends easily

2. Which of the following might a child *caress?*
   (a) a baby sister   (c) a pet rabbit
   (b) a stuffed animal   (d) a porcupine

3. Which of the following might a person *clutch?*
   (a) a phone call   (c) a baseball bat
   (b) a telephone   (d) a baseball score

4. Which of the following is a friendly *gesture?*
   (a) sending a get-well card   (c) holding out your hand
   (b) closing your eyes   (d) turning your back

5. Which of the following might a person who is *moping* do?
   (a) suggest having a party   (c) stay home all day
   (b) not answer when spoken to   (d) call up old friends

6. Which of the following could be *recovered?*
   (a) lost time   (c) your balance
   (b) a lost ring   (d) your health

7. Which of the following can be *replaced?*
   (a) a book taken from the shelf   (c) a friend who dies
   (b) a lost screwdriver   (d) a pet turtle that dies

8. Who would someone be likely to *shun?*
   (a) an enemy   (c) a friend
   (b) an untrustworthy person   (d) a helpful person

12D Completing the Thought

Read each sentence below and fill in the blank with the correct word (or a form of the word) from the word list.

1. Carlos wanted to go to the ball game, but Maria talked him out of it because she wanted to spend their day off at the pool. That was usually her _____.

2. Randy spent at least fifteen minutes trying to get Tibbles to try the new cat food he had bought. Tibbles would have none of it, though, no matter how much Randy _____.

3. Every time I wiped the baby's mouth with a wash cloth, she screamed until her whole face was purple! She was absolutely _____.

4. Henri was upset because his brother had gotten the laundry pile mixed up with the clothes that were supposed to go to the cleaner. He always kept the laundry and the dry cleaning _____.

| ability |
| amiable |
| bliss |
| caress |
| clutch |
| coax |
| furious |
| prefer |
| request |
| separate |

5. The new mother sat with her baby in her arms, rocking slowly. Her expression was
   _____.

6. Sarah's driving teacher told her to relax when he saw her holding the steering wheel so tightly
   that her knuckles were white. "Try not to _____ the wheel," he said.

7. Since the tables overlooking the park always fill up first, it's a good idea to get to Davio's early.
   Then you can _____ a parkside table.

8. When Mozart was a child, not only could he play the piano beautifully, but he could also write
   music for the orchestra. He had rare musical _____.

9. Rosie had spent the afternoon doing what she liked best, lying in the hammock with a good
   book to keep her company while the birds sang overhead. Maybe that explains why she was so
   _____ at dinner.

10. Rebecca was a wonderful baby-sitter. She could always calm a crying baby with a gentle
    _____.

12E Narrative

Read the narrative below; then complete the exercise that follows.

COMMUNICATING WITH KOKO

American Sign Language (ASL) is a form of communication that is as rich and flexible as spoken English. It is used by hundreds of thousands of hearing-impaired people. Each **gesture** of the hand or arm has a particular meaning. In the early 1970s, a most unusual student began learning to communicate through ASL. Her name was Koko and her teacher was Dr. Francine Patterson.

Koko is a gorilla who was born in the San Francisco Zoo. While still a baby, she became ill and had to be **separated** from the other gorillas. She lived in a specially equipped trailer, where Dr. Patterson, a scientist interested in animal behavior, took care of her. While Dr. Patterson was nursing Koko back to health she slowly and with great difficulty taught the young gorilla to communicate, using ASL hand and arm movements.

Dr. Patterson made up little games to teach Koko how to use her hands. She began by working on words for food and drink, showing her the object, saying the word, and making the sign. For example, she would sign the word for drink before giving Koko a drink. Koko began to show signs that she understood the meaning of Dr. Patterson's gestures after only two weeks. Once she made the association between hand movements and the objects they represented, she quickly began to learn words. By eighteen months, she knew twenty-two signs; by three years and three months she could make seventy-eight understandable signs. Over a period of six years, she learned over a thousand words and could even string words together to form simple sentences.

Dr. Patterson also used picture books to teach Koko new words. Koko **preferred** looking at books with pictures of gorillas and cats, so when Dr. Patterson asked Koko what she wanted for her birthday, she wasn't surprised when Koko **requested** a cat. Koko was usually a very **amiable** creature, but when she opened Dr. Patterson's present and saw a stuffed animal, she was **furious** and threw it away. Dr. Patterson tried to **coax** the unhappy gorilla to play with the toy cat, but her attempts failed. Koko knew the difference between a real cat and a toy one, and she **shunned** the stuffed animal completely. She wanted a real cat.

A few weeks later Dr. Patterson gave Koko a little gray kitten. Koko picked up the kitten very carefully and **caressed** it gently. When asked what she was going to call it, she signed "All Ball." Perhaps she gave it this name because it had no tail, and without a tail it looked just like a ball of fur. As Koko carried All Ball around on her back, the kitten **clutched** Koko's fur, the way baby gorillas do with their mothers. Koko loved to play games with All Ball; the two became close friends.

One day All Ball was hit by a car and died. For days afterward, Koko **moped**—miserable over the loss of her friend. Koko **recovered** her good spirits when Dr. Patterson gave her another kitten to **replace** All Ball. When Koko got her new pet, she picked it up and held it lovingly, a **blissful** look on her face.

With language comes the **ability** to make jokes—and also to lie. Koko learned to do both. One day she broke the sink in the trailer. When Dr. Patterson asked her who had done it, Koko signed the name of the person who had been in the trailer with her. Another time she pointed to a white towel and signed "red." She was corrected several times but refused to admit she had made a mistake. Then she slyly picked a tiny piece of lint off the towel. It was red!

Answer each of the following questions in a sentence. If a question does not contain a vocabulary word, use a vocabulary word in your answer. Use each word only once. Questions and answers will then contain all fifteen words (or forms of the words) from this lesson's word list.

1. What is the meaning of **gesture** as it is used in the narrative?

   _____

2. Why was Koko living in a trailer?

   _____

3. Did Koko show a **preference** for a particular kind of book?

   _____

4. Why did Dr. Patterson choose a cat to give Koko?

   _____

5. What kind of personality did Koko have?

   _____

6. What is the meaning of **furious** as it is used in the narrative?

   _____

7. How did Koko respond to Dr. Patterson's **coaxing?**

   _____

8. Why did Koko **shun** the toy cat?

   _____

9. How did Koko show that she cherished the real kitten?

   _____

10. How did All Ball stay on Koko's back?

    _____

11. How could Dr. Patterson tell that Koko was sad when All Ball died?

    _____

12. What is the meaning of **replace** as it is used in the narrative?

_____

13. How could Dr. Patterson tell that Koko was happy with the second cat?

_____

14. What did learning to communicate allow Koko to do?

_____

15. What kind of thing would make you feel **blissful**?

_____

WORDLY WISE

You are likely to **caress** those who are most dear to you. This is not surprising, since the word comes from the Latin *caro*, which means "dear." You might think that the word *care* comes from this same Latin root since we care for those who are dear to us, but it comes from something totally different: the Old English word *cearu*.

The noun **clutch** has an unusual meaning when it is used as the plural noun *clutches*. To be "in the clutches" of something or somebody is to be in the power of that thing or that person. People who are taken hostage are in the *clutches* of those who have taken them prisoner; criminals spend a lot of time trying to avoid the *clutches* of the law.

HIDDEN MESSAGE

In the boxes provided, write the words from Lessons 9 through 12 that are missing in each of the sentences below. The number following each sentence gives the word list from which the missing word is taken. When the exercise is finished, the shaded boxes should spell out an interesting observation from the English writer, philosopher, and mathematician, Bertrand Russell.

1. She has a well-deserved _____ for being fair. (9)

2. The _____ in my leg is healing quickly. (11)

3. We all _____ for those who died in the accident. (9)

4. These are some _____ nails left over from the job. (9)

5. I don't _____ people who work nights. (9)

6. I stood on the edge of the _____ and looked down. (10)

7. We tried to _____ him for the loss of his pet rabbit. (10)

8. This year's _____ meeting will be held in May. (11)

9. After a year's hard work, I was able to _____ my place on the team. (10)

10. When food is _____ , people can go hungry. (9)

11. I will _____ all my spare time to caring for my grandmother. (9)

12. Dara offered the visitors a plate of _____ little sandwiches. (9)

13. The magician promised us that her next trick would _____ us. (9)

14. We built a _____ shelter from cardboard boxes. (11)

15. My wages will _____ from $200 to $250 a week. (11)

16. Their calm manner helped _____ our fears. (10)

17. My brother has the _____ to become an excellent singer. (12)

18. The sun's warmth causes the water to _____ . (11)

19. The entertainers will _____ before a live audience. (9)

20. A headache could be a _____ of flu. (10)

21. My _____ came from buying and selling cars. (10)

22. The breeze was gentle as a _____ on their faces. (12)

23. We tried to _____ them into staying a little longer. (12)

24. David was able to _____ Goliath with a slingshot. (10)

25. The photograph provided _____ proof of our stay. (11)

26. We stayed in _____ rooms at the hotel. (12)

27. Annie Lennox gets thousands of _____ for her autograph. (12)

28. The _____ of the water is about ten feet. (10)

29. I had the _____ to lose my suitcase when I changed trains. (10)

30. Andros and Helen made a _____ effort to help the new students. (10)

31. The cause of my _____ puzzled the doctors. (10)

32. The trees lose their _____ in the fall. (11)

33. The host's _____ manner put us at ease. (12)

34. My dad was _____ with me for lying to him. (12)

35. We did not _____ from danger. (9)

36. The rose was of a pale yellow _____ . (11)

37. This is a _____ of Brazilian and Kenyan coffees. (11)

38. I prefer real flowers to _____ ones. (11)

39. What you earn at the print shop will _____ from week to week. (11)

40. The doctor said my uncle would _____ very quickly. (12)

41. When I have nothing to read on vacations, I sometimes _____ . (12)

42. I felt the person next to me _____ my arm. (12)

43. The police officer _____ to us to cross the street. (12)

44. It would _____ me to listen to the same story again. (11)

45. It was _____ to lie on the beach without a care. (12)

46. Do you _____ spinach or broccoli? (12)

47. Allow me to _____ this new computer program. (9)

48. _____ fatty foods if you want to stay healthy. (12)

49. We usually _____ by letter. (10)

50. What do you _____ to do about the problem? (9)

51. Why does the dog _____ when you approach it? (10)

52. You need to _____ the damaged parts. (12)

53. This field should _____ two tons of potatoes. (11)

54. My greatest _____ was to complete college. (10)

55. I asked some fifth graders to help _____ the meeting. (9)

56. My _____ in the chess match was a very good player. (9)

Lesson 13

Word List

Study the definitions of the words below; then do the exercises for the lesson.

appal
 v. To cause horror, shock, or dismay.
 [The inspectors were *appalled* by the conditions in the prison factories.]
 appalling *adj.* Causing shock and horror.
 [The television report exposed the *appalling* treatment of the farm workers.]

dejected
 adj. Discouraged; low in spirits.
 [Jesse felt *dejected* when he couldn't find an apartment with low rent.]

depend
 v. 1. To rely on for support.
 [Many blind persons *depend* on guide dogs.]
 2. To be based on.
 [Whether or not I go to the concert *depends* on what my parents say.]
 dependable *adj.* Reliable.
 [If you do a lot of driving, you need a *dependable* car.]

dreary
 adj. Sad and gloomy.
 [I pulled up the shades to let more light into Olga's dark and *dreary* apartment.]

fanatic
 n. A person whose enthusiasm for a belief is extreme.
 [Jim Jones was a religious *fanatic* who persuaded hundreds of his followers to kill themselves.]
 adj. Carrying an interest or enthusiasm to extremes.
 [Mr. Gradgrind was a *fanatical* believer in the importance of facts.]

impact
 n. 1. The striking of one object by another.
 [The *impact* of the ball bruised the catcher's arm.]
 2. Forceful impression.
 [Martin Luther King's "I Have a Dream" speech had a great *impact* on millions of Americans.]

invade
 v. 1. To enter by force in order to take over.
 [The German army *invaded* Russia in June, 1941.]
 2. To intrude; to enter in great numbers.
 [I am putting a lock on my drawer so my little sister won't be able to *invade* my privacy any more.]
 invasion *n.* The act of invading.
 [The gypsy moth *invasion* caused the destruction of many Cape Cod pine trees.]

isolate
 v. To cut off from others.
 [As soon as my brother broke out in spots the doctor *isolated* him for a week.]
 isolation *n.* The condition of being isolated.
 [The cottage's *isolation* makes it appealing to someone seeking a quiet vacation.]
 isolated *adj.* Cut off from others.
 [The lighthouse keeper actually enjoyed her *isolated* life.]

occupy   *v.* 1. To live in; to take up.
[My Aunt Bianca's family *occupied* the apartment next to us when I was little.]
2. To take over by force.
[Protesting students *occupied* the school president's office.]
occupation   *n.* 1. A person's job or profession.
[Nursing is a perfect *occupation* for my brother since he loves helping people.]
2. A filling up of time or space.
[The sign in the elevator said that *occupation* by more than twelve people was against the law.]

reveal   *v.* 1. To make known.
[If you *reveal* the wish you made, it might not come true.]
2. To bring into view; to show.
[The curtain rose to *reveal* three men sitting on top of a stone wall.]

rout   *n.* A disorganized retreat from an attack; a total defeat.
[The battle ended in a *rout* as the enemy soldiers dropped their weapons and ran.]
v. To defeat completely.
[The U.S. basketball players *routed* their opponents in the 1992 Olympic Games.]

suspect   *v.* 1. To think of as probably guilty.
[The police *suspect* the man who used to live upstairs of breaking in to our apartment.]
2. To suppose that something is true.
[I *suspect* that she knows more algebra than she thinks she does.]
n. A person believed to be guilty.
[The *suspect* asked to see a lawyer before being questioned.]

temporary   *adj.* Lasting or made to last for a short time.
[The town hall provided a *temporary* place for people to stay during the hurricane.]

terror   *n.* Great fear.
[Thunder and lightning always fill my grandmother with *terror*.]
terrify   *v.* To fill with terror or great fear.
[The reports of the crime in the neighborhood *terrified* the residents.]

tragic   *adj.* Causing great sadness; terrible or dreadful.
[The entire nation grieved over the *tragic* death of Dr. Martin Luther King, Jr.]
tragedy   *n.* 1. An event that causes great pain, suffering, or loss of life.
[The closing of the shipyard would be a *tragedy* for Charlestown.]
2. A play that ends sadly as the hero or heroine loses at the end of a great struggle.
[Shakespeare wrote some of the world's greatest *tragedies*.]

13A Finding Meanings

Choose two phrases to form a sentence that correctly uses a word from Word List 13. Write each sentence in the space provided.

1. (a) travel through it.
   (b) live in it.

   (c) To isolate a place is to
   (d) To occupy a place is to

2. (a) A dependable person   (c) takes things in stride.
    (b) A dejected person   (d) is in low spirits.

3. (a) Impact is   (c) a desire to do good.
    (b) a forceful impression.   (d) Terror is

4. (a) rely on that person.   (c) play a joke on that person.
    (b) To appal someone is to   (d) To depend on someone is to

5. (a) To reveal a place is to   (c) make changes in it.
    (b) To invade a place is to   (d) enter it to take over.

6. (a) well cared for.   (c) cut off from others.
    (b) To be fanatic is to be   (d) To be isolated is to be

7. (a) To suspect something is to   (c) be afraid of it.
    (b) bring it into view.   (d) To reveal something is to

8. (a) A dreary event is one   (c) that lasts a short time.
    (b) that causes great sadness.   (d) A tragic event is one

9. (a) To suspect someone is to   (c) make fun of that person.
    (b) believe that person to be guilty.   (d) To appal someone is to

10. (a) A rout is   (c) a path that is traveled.
     (b) one who has extreme beliefs.   (d) A fanatic is

13B Just the Right Word

Improve each of the following sentences by crossing out the italicized phrase and replacing it with a word (or a form of the word) from Word List 13.

1. Whether or not I go on the trip to the mountains will *be based* on the condition of my car.

2. The school building seems *dull and gloomy* during winter vacation.

3. A person with measles should be *kept away from other people.*

4. My job making pizza is *not expected to last for very long,* but I love it.

5. I was *shocked and dismayed* to find out that my neighbors had had no heat in their house for four days.

6. When cockroaches *moved in and took over* our kitchen, my mother called the landlord immediately.

7 The detective waited to question the *persons believed to be guilty of the crime* until their lawyer arrived.

8. There was a look of *great fear* in her eyes as she heard the crash of thunder.

9. The Red Sox *completely defeated* the Yankees by a score of 10 to 0.

10. *Hamlet* is one of Shakespeare's most famous *plays that end sadly as the hero loses at the end of a great struggle.*

13C Applying Meanings

Circle the letter of each correct answer to the questions below. A question may have more than one correct answer.

1. Which of the following should you be able to *depend* on?
   (a) a close friend
   (b) your parents
   (c) a stranger
   (d) a scoundrel

2. Which of the following could you *reveal?*
   (a) your age
   (b) your date of birth
   (c) your weight
   (d) your plans for the future

3. Which final basketball score(s) would be a *rout?*
   (a) 102 to 98   (c) 110 to 108
   (b) 68 to 12   (d) 72 to 10

4. Which of the following might be thought *dreary?*
   (a) a blissful afternoon   (c) an afternoon spent pulling up weeds
   (b) a bright hue   (d) a person who lacks a sense of humor

5. Which of the following could be *temporary?*
   (a) a death   (c) a shelter
   (b) a job   (d) a period without rain

6. Which of the following would have an *impact?*
   (a) the death of a president   (c) the loss of one's job
   (b) a leaf landing on the ground   (d) a car hitting a tree

7. Which of the following might be *appalling?*
   (a) an increase in crime   (c) the condition of homeless people
   (b) world hunger   (d) the number of people in prison

8. Which of the following is an *occupation?*
   (a) poet   (c) uncle
   (b) lawyer   (d) teacher

13D Completing the Thought

Read each sentence below and fill in the blank with the correct word (or a form of the word) from the word list.

dejected
depend
fanatic
invade
isolate
occupy
reveal
suspect
terror
tragic

1. When Ms. Delano got on the bus, she was dismayed to find that there was nowhere to sit, so she had to stand. All the seats were
   _____.

2. Shakespeare's *Romeo and Juliet* ends with the death of the two young lovers. *Romeo and Juliet* is a _____.

3. The Suns use Samantha to baby-sit for their two-year-old because she always shows up and is never late. Samantha is very
   _____.

4. The newspapers were filled with reports of a coming earthquake. People were living in _____.

5. The head nurse has trained everyone to wash carefully before touching a patient. She is _____ about cleanliness.

6. When my father saw the chocolate around my sister's mouth, he thought he knew who ate the last piece of cake. She was the most likely _____.

7. The vet took one look at the farmer's sick cow and immediately separated it from the rest of the herd. It had to be _____.

8. There was nothing that Clara's friends could do to cheer her up so they decided to leave her alone. She was very _____.

9. In 1940, the British people were afraid that the German army might land on their shores. They were very worried about a possible _____.

10. You can count on Mom to keep a secret. She'll never _____ it.

13E Narrative

Read the narrative below; then complete the exercise that follows.

ANNE FRANK'S DIARY

Anne Frank was eleven years old in 1940 when the armies of Adolf Hitler, the Nazi ruler of Germany, **invaded** Holland, where she lived with her parents and her older sister. The Frank family was Jewish. They were **appalled** by Hitler's **fanatic** hatred of Jews and his plan to murder all the Jews in the countries he could control.

For two years, Anne Frank and her family lived in daily **terror** of being rounded up and taken away. Finally, the family, together with Anne's friend Peter and three others, went into hiding. Eight people **occupied** a tiny space hidden behind a bookshelf in Mr. Frank's office. They **depended** on brave friends who brought them food and news of the outside world. They hoped that Hitler would soon be defeated and their stay would be **temporary**, but after two more long years they were still in hiding.

From 1942 to 1944 Anne Frank kept a diary in which she wrote about the things that happened every day and their **impact** on her life. Although life in these cramped surroundings was very **dreary**, Anne's diary is always interesting. In it she **reveals** her deepest thoughts and feelings. She complains of the feelings of **isolation** they all had, and she writes of their hopes of one day leading a normal life. No matter how **dejected** she felt, she always made the effort to keep the diary up-to-date.

Being discovered by the Germans was Anne Frank's greatest fear. Any unusual sounds from outside—slamming doors, heavy footsteps, German voices—could be a sign of danger. The little group had the use of a toilet, but they could not flush it during the day because someone in the building might hear it and **suspect** that people were hiding in that tiny space behind the bookshelves.

World War II ended in 1945, when Hitler's armies were **routed** in the East by the Russians and in the West by the Americans and the British. Sadly, its end came too late for Anne Frank. The Germans had found the family's hiding place the year before. Everyone was sent to Hitler's death camps, and it was in one of them, in March 1945, two months before the end of the war in Europe, that Anne died. She was sixteen years old.

We would not know of her **tragic** story but for her diary. She left it behind when she was taken away, and a friend of the family found it and kept it. After the war, Anne's father, who managed to stay alive while in the Nazi death camp, returned home. When he discovered Anne had been killed, the friend of the family gave the diary to him.

Answer each of the following questions in a sentence. If a question does not contain a vocabulary word, use a vocabulary word in your answer. Use each word only once. Questions and answers will then contain all fifteen words (or forms of the words) from this lesson's word list.

1. What part of Anne Frank's story had the greatest **impact** on you?

   _____

2. What terrible misfortune happened to the people of Holland in 1940?

   _____

3. Why is Hitler such an **appalling** figure in the world's history?

   _____

4. What was the main reason for Hitler's actions?

   _____

5. Why did the European Jews fear the Germans?

   _____

6. What is the meaning of **occupied** as it is used in the narrative?

   _____

7. How did Anne Frank's family and friends get food?

   _____

8. Why did those in hiding think their stay might be **temporary**?

_____

9. What might those in hiding have done to make life less **dreary**?

_____

10. Why do you think readers of her diary feel so close to Anne Frank?

_____

11. Why do you think those in hiding complained of feeling **isolated**?

_____

12. At what times do you think Anne Frank might have been most **dejected**?

_____

13. What made it possible for the Frank group to stay hidden for two years?

_____

14. Why was 1945 Adolph Hitler's worst year?

_____

15. Why is Anne Frank's story such a **tragic** one?

_____

WORDLY WISE

The adjective **isolated** comes from the Latin *solus,* which means "alone; without company." *Isolated* suggests being cut off from others. A young child starting a new school may feel *isolated,* that is, lonely and cut off from old friends. An island far from any other land could be called an *isolated* spot.

The adjective **temporary** comes from the Latin *tempus,* which means "time." A *temporary* job is one that is not expected to last for very long. The antonym of this word is *permanent.* A *permanent* job is one that can be expected to last for a long time.

Lesson 14

Word List

Study the definitions of the words below; then do the exercises for the lesson.

afford
v. 1. To be able to pay for.
[Can you *afford* a new pair of running shoes?]
2. To be able to do.
[When you're on the soccer team, you can't *afford* to miss a night's sleep.]
3. To give; to provide.
[Music *affords* me much pleasure.]

boast
v. 1. To talk with too much pride in oneself or in what one owns or has done; to brag.
[Ben *boasted* about all the Scrabble games he had won.]
2. To have and to take a proper pride in having.
[San Francisco *boasts* one of the finest bridges in the word, the Golden Gate Bridge.]
boast *n.* An act of boasting.
["It was just a *boast*," Julio said. "I can't really run five miles."]

chord
n. Two or more notes of music played together.
[Becca played a few *chords* on the guitar.]

exceptional
adj. Unusually good.
[The batik cloth was of *exceptional* quality.]

fortunate
adj. Lucky.
[You are *fortunate* to have such kind friends.]

fringe
n. 1. An edge made of short lengths of material such as thread, used to decorate clothes, curtains, etc.
[My skirt had a *fringe* down the side.]
2. An outside edge.
[At the concert, I stood at the *fringe* of the crowd.]

humble
adj. 1. Plain and simple.
[Abraham Lincoln was raised in a *humble* log cabin.]
2. Not proud; modest.
[In her *humble* speech of thanks, the new mayor said she would need all the help she could get.]
v. To bring down to defeat.
[We *humbled* Newton High, our opponent in Saturday's game.]

meadow
n. A field of grass or wildflowers.
[In the middle of the *meadow* stood a cow and its calf.]

melancholy
adj. Filled with sorrow; very sad.
[The movie was so sad it left me in a *melancholy* mood.]
n. A state of sadness.
[His *melancholy* began to affect my mood and I grew more and more dejected.]

obstinate	*adj.* Not willing to give in; stubborn. [You can't persuade him to do anything—he's too *obstinate*.]
plead	*v.* 1. To ask for something that is felt to be very important; to beg. [The family *pleaded* with reporters to leave them alone.] 2. To respond to a charge by a court of law. [The prisoner said he wished to *plead* not guilty.]
plunge	*v.* 1. To throw oneself into. [We *plunged* into the pool and swam a few laps.] 2. To push or force quickly. [I *plunged* the spade into the earth.] 3. To drop sharply. [The price of land near the new dump *plunged* last year.] *n.* A sudden dive or fall. [My spirits took a *plunge* when I saw the first page of the test.]
relent	*v.* To become less strict. [My parents finally *relented* and said I could go to the concert.]
submit	*v.* 1. To give to someone to look over or decide about. [Each student is asked to *submit* a picture for the yearbook.] 2. To give in to someone or something. [My sister was always telling me what to do, but I refused to *submit* to her.]
trudge	*v.* To walk slowly and heavily, as though with great effort. [We had to *trudge* through deep snow to reach the door.]

14A Finding Meanings

Choose two phrases to form a sentence that correctly uses a word from Word List 14. Write each sentence in the space provided.

1. (a) Fortunate people
   (b) Humble people
   (c) are not vain.
   (d) change their minds easily.

_____

2. (a) three or more notes played together.
   (b) an edging of short lengths of material.
   (c) A plunge is
   (d) A chord is

_____

3. (a) A fortunate person is one
   (b) who is lucky.
   (c) who suffers from poor health.
   (d) A melancholy person is one

_____

4. (a) A boast is
   (b) A meadow is
   (c) a grassy field.
   (d) a steep hill.

_____

5. (a) beg for something.   (c) To plead is to
   (b) deny something.   (d) To submit is to

6. (a) To boast a fine sports stadium   (c) is to take good care of it.
   (b) To afford a fine sports stadium   (d) is to take pride in it.

7. (a) An exceptional student is one who   (c) is very lucky.
   (b) An obstinate student is one who   (d) has great ability.

8. (a) a sharp drop.   (c) A plunge is
   (b) a change of mind.   (d) A fringe is

9. (a) give it to someone for approval.   (c) To submit something is to
   (b) To afford something is to   (d) be ashamed of it.

10. (a) Obstinate people   (c) are unable to make up their minds.
    (b) Melancholy people   (d) are unwilling to change their minds.

14B Just the Right Word

Improve each of the following sentences by crossing out the italicized phrase and replacing it with a word (or a form of the word) from Word List 14.

1. Raoul had no choice but to *give in* to his parents' rules.

2. After you *say, when asked by the judge, that you are* innocent, the trial will begin.

3. Our first apartment was *plain and simple*, but we loved it.

4. It was Aunt Oona's *proud claim* that she could run two miles in twelve minutes.

5. At first Mom said we couldn't ride our bikes to the movies, but after thinking it over she *changed her mind and said that we could.*

6. Neema and Bill *walked slowly and with much effort* up the steep path to the top of Corey Hill.

7. The crowd gasped as the Olympic swimmer *dived suddenly* into the pool.

8. I prefer the tan lampshade with the *edge of short lengths of thread sewn on for decoration*.

9. We were all wondering how Alisa could *spare the money for* all those new clothes.

10. The second movement of the Brahms symphony fills me with *feelings of great sadness*.

14C Applying Meanings

Circle the letter of each correct answer to the questions below. A question may have more than one correct answer.

1. Which of the following might a person *boast* about?
   - (a) cheating
   - (b) losing
   - (c) winning
   - (d) failing

2. Which of the following might make a person feel *fortunate*?
   - (a) having good health
   - (b) having kind parents
   - (c) living in a free country
   - (d) getting free tickets to the circus

3. Which of the following might have a *fringe*?
   - (a) a crowd
   - (b) a lake
   - (c) a blanket
   - (d) a story

4. Which of the following might be too much for most people to *afford*?
   - (a) to go on a trip around the world
   - (b) to spare some time
   - (c) to miss a meal
   - (d) to buy a sports car

5. Which of the following can be *humble*?
   - (a) a person
   - (b) a cottage
   - (c) a speech
   - (d) a palace

6. Which of the following might you find in a *meadow*?
   - (a) cows
   - (b) picnickers
   - (c) wildflowers
   - (d) skyscrapers

7. Which of the following might a person *plead* for?
   - (a) more help
   - (b) more money
   - (c) mercy
   - (d) misfortune

8. Which of the following can *plunge*?
   - (a) the temperature
   - (b) the price of a house
   - (c) a rock
   - (d) the age of a house

14D Completing the Thought

Read each sentence below and fill in the blank with the correct word (or a form of the word) from the word list.

1. When Connie and her mother missed the bus, they had to walk three miles in the pouring rain. By the time they neared home, they were _____ along, soaked to the skin.

2. José got straight A's, was class president, and editor of the school newspaper. He was a(n) _____ student.

3. Tokoyo stood on the edge of the precipice for a moment and then leaped into the water far below. It was a courageous _____.

4. At his first guitar lesson, Miguel's teacher taught him how to make a pleasant sound by playing three notes together. Miguel was learning _____.

chord
exceptional
fringe
humble
melancholy
obstinate
plunge
relent
submit
trudge

5. Before Jerry could get a library card, he had to show the librarian something with his name and address on it. He had to _____ proof that he lived in Yonkers.

6. Joel repeatedly refused to lend Mike his fishing equipment even though he wasn't using it and Mike promised to take care of it. Joel was very _____.

7. Jane and I were trying to figure out how to make her skirt longer. We decided to add some _____.

8. Billy had been told over and over that it was out of the question, but he was sure that his parents would change their minds and let him have a dirt bike. He knew they would _____.

9. The play had such an unhappy ending and yet was so moving that we left the theater feeling thoughtful and sad at the same time. We were filled with _____.

10. Even though she was probably one of the best and busiest surgeons in the country, she was always ready to talk to you. She was a modest, _____ person.

14E Narrative

Read the narrative below; then complete the exercise that follows.

HOW WATER LILIES BEGAN

This is a folktale from Wales, a small country west of England. It tells how water lilies came to grow in a lake in the Welsh mountains. It was all because of Huw, a farmer's son who loved to play the harp and never went to school. Huw lived with his mother in a **humble** cottage by the side of a mountain. Every morning, he drove his mother's black and white cows up the mountain, where they spent the day in a **meadow** by the side of the lake.

One day, Huw took his harp and played a few **chords** as he watched over the herd. To his astonishment, six silver cows rose out of the water, drawn by the music. Their coats gleamed in the sunlight as they gathered around Huw and listened to him play. They stayed with the herd all day, following the rest of the cows back to the farm that evening. Huw's mother felt very **fortunate** to have such fine new cows. She **boasted** to her neighbors that they gave twice as much milk as the black and white ones. And, she added, the milk was of **exceptional** quality.

All went well until one of the silver cows stopped giving milk. After waiting a few days, Huw's mother told the butcher to come the next day and take the cow away. Huw **pleaded** with his mother to spare the animal, but she wouldn't **relent**. She told Huw that they couldn't **afford** to have even one cow eating grass and giving nothing in return. The boy knew how **obstinate** his mother could be once her mind was made up, but he argued with her for as long as he dared. When his mother told him to be quiet, he knew he had no choice but to **submit** to her will.

The next morning, as he **trudged** up the mountain, Huw could think of nothing but the beautiful silver cow that was going to be sold. The music he played on his harp that day became increasingly **melancholy** until at last, his eyes filled with tears, he could play no more. He stood up and threw his harp into the lake. At once a strange thing happened. The six silver cows ran to the edge of the lake and **plunged** in. They were never seen again.

Soon masses of silver water lilies began to grow all along the **fringes** of the lake where the silver cows had jumped in. They still grow there today. Huw's mother died long ago, and Huw is now an old man. If you should meet him and tell him you don't believe this story, he will be happy to take you up the mountain and show you the beautiful silver water lilies.

Answer each of the following questions in a sentence. If a question does not contain a vocabulary word, use a vocabulary word in your answer. Use each word only once. Questions and answers will then contain all fifteen words (or forms of the words) from this lesson's word list.

1. Why might it be easy to pick the water lilies that grew in the lake?

   _____

2. How did the music Huw played match his mood?

   _____

3. What is the meaning of **afford** as it is used in the narrative?

   _____

4. How can you tell that Huw's family was not wealthy?

   _____

5. How can you tell from the narrative that Huw's mother was not a shy person?

   _____

6. Where did Huw and the cows go every day?

   _____

7. What did the silver cows seem to be responding to?

   _____

8. Why was milk from the silver cows worth more than milk from the other cows?

   _____

9. Why did Huw's mother feel **fortunate** to have the silver cows?

   _____

10. How can you tell from the narrative that Huw was unwilling to defy his mother?

    _____

11. What did Huw do when his mother said the butcher would take the cow?

    _____

12. Did Huw's mother agree to do what he asked?

    _____

13. What does the word **trudged** suggest about Huw's feelings as he went up the mountain?

_____

14. Why was it a waste of time for Huw to argue with his mother?

_____

15. What was the last glimpse that Huw had of the silver cows?

_____

WORDLY WISE

Chord has another meaning in addition to the one given. In geometry, a *chord* is a straight line joining any two points on a circle.

Chord and *cord* are homonyms. *Cord* is thick string or twine. It is also a unit of measurement; a *cord* of firewood is a stack that measures eight feet by four feet by four feet.

In the Middle Ages, over five hundred years ago, people believed that the human body contained four different kinds of fluids, called *humors*. The four humors were blood, phlegm, yellow bile, and black bile. When these were in balance, a person was said to be in good humor; when they were out of balance, a person's mood was affected. Too much blood made a person *sanguine,* or cheerful (the Latin word for blood is *sanguis).* Too much phlegm made a person *phlegmatic,* or slow to respond. Too much yellow bile, called *choler,* made a person *choleric,* or angry. Too much black bile, called *melan choler* made a person **melancholy,** or unhappy.

Lesson 15

Word List

Study the definitions of the words below; then do the exercises for the lesson.

apparent
adj. 1. Clear.
[It's *apparent* that no one's home.]
2. Seeming or appearing to be.
[The *apparent* cause of increase in the price of lettuce was the spring freeze.]

ban
v. To forbid, especially by passing a law or making a rule.
[The hospital *bans* smoking anywhere in the building.]
n. A law or rule that forbids something.
[Included in the 1994 Crime Bill was a *ban* on handguns.]

concentrate
v. 1. To focus all one's thoughts or efforts on.
[It's hard for me to *concentrate* on homework when I hear the kids outside.]
2. To bring or come together in one place.
[Factories were *concentrated* along the east side of the Harlem River.]
concentration *n.* Giving total attention to something.
[Don't sing! It ruins my *concentration*.]
concentrated *adj.* Of increased strength or thickness.
[For breakfast, mix one part of *concentrated* orange juice to three parts water.]

concern
v. 1. To be about; to interest.
[Homelessness is a subject that should *concern* everyone.]
2. To trouble or worry.
[My parents are *concerned* about my brother's health.]
n. 1. Something that involves a person or people.
[Health care is a big *concern* for most people.]
2. A business organization.
[After college she got a job with a banking *concern*.]

consider
v. 1. To think about carefully.
[Since my teaching job is a temporary one, it's time to *consider* what I should do next.]
2. To take into account.
[Please *consider* my feelings when you comment on the story I wrote.]
3. To believe.
[I may only be seventeen, but I *consider* myself an adult.]

contrast
v. 1. To compare in order to show the differences.
[Before deciding on the design for the new gym, we are going to *contrast* the two proposed plans.]
2. To show differences when compared.
[His actions *contrast* greatly with his words.]
n. A difference.
[Our new apartment is a welcome *contrast* to our old one.]

fragile
adj. Easily broken or damaged.
[This antique chair is so *fragile* that it would break if anyone sat on it.]

menace	*n.* Something that is likely to do harm or is regarded as dangerous. [Icebergs are a *menace* to ships in the North Atlantic.] *v.* To be a danger to; to put at risk. [The approaching hurricane *menaces* the entire South Carolina coast.]
pounce	*v.* To swoop down on and seize. [The cat *pounced* on the mouse as soon as it ventured from its hole.]
prompt	*adj.* Quick; without too much time passing. [I sent a *prompt* reply to Ahmed's letter.] *v.* To cause to act. [Seeing ants all over the counter *prompted* me to spend the afternoon cleaning the kitchen.]
recent	*adj.* Of a time just before the present. [The *recent* outbreak of measles resulted in the temporary closing of our school.]
symbol	*n.* Something that stands for something else. [The dove is a *symbol* of peace.]
talon	*n.* The claw of a bird, usually one that kills animals for food. [The hawk clutched its victim firmly in its *talons*.]
trophy	*n.* Something, as a prize or award, given to show success in an activity. [The Heisman *trophy* is a top football honor.]
widespread	*adj.* 1. Spread or stretched out over a large area. [The *widespread* wings of the condor can reach ten feet from tip to tip.] 2. Happening or found over a large area. [There was *widespread* frost last night.]

15A Finding Meanings

Choose two phrases to form a sentence that correctly uses a word from Word List 15. Write each sentence in the space provided.

1. (a) total attention.
   (b) a lack of interest.
   (c) Concern is
   (d) Concentration is

   _____

2. (a) An apparent winner is
   (b) one who always wins.
   (c) A recent winner is
   (d) one who seems to have won.

   _____

3. (a) A concern is
   (b) A symbol is
   (c) a business organization.
   (d) something that is likely to do harm.

   _____

4. (a) To concentrate things is to   (c) To pounce is to
    (b) become scarce.   (d) bring them together in one place.

---

5. (a) took place a short time ago.   (c) A widespread storm is one that
    (b) A recent storm is one that   (d) lasted for just a short time.

---

6. (a) A contrast is   (c) a rule that forbids something.
    (b) an unintended result.   (d) A ban is

---

7. (a) To prompt something is   (c) to be a danger to it.
    (b) To menace something is   (d) to allow it to happen.

---

8. (a) to show how they differ.   (c) To consider two things is
    (b) To contrast two things is   (d) to prefer one over the other.

---

9. (a) found all over.   (c) Something that is widespread is
    (b) broken into pieces.   (d) Something that is fragile is

---

10. (a) To prompt something is to   (c) To consider something is to
    (b) take it into account.   (d) forbid it.

---

11. (a) A trophy is   (c) something that stands for something else.
    (b) A symbol is   (d) an animal's claw.

15B Just the Right Word

Improve each of the following sentences by crossing out the italicized phrase and replacing it with a word (or a form of the word) from Word List 15.

1. My grandmother's teacups are too *easily broken* to use every day.

2. The kitten *leaped through the air and landed* on the ball of yarn.

3. Hearing about a new play being put on *caused* me to try out for one of the parts.

4. The eagle's *sharp, curved claws* grasped the fish and lifted it out of the water.

5. Her golfing *award for victory* was the thing she took great pride in.

6. Chapter 5 *points out the differences between* school life today and that of a century ago.

7. *Keep your mind only* on your driving and forget about looking at the scenery.

8. Have you *given any thought to* trading in your old car for a new one?

9. My grandmother's future is a subject that *is of great interest to* my parents.

15C Applying Meanings

Circle the letter of each correct answer to the questions below. A question may have more than one correct answer.

1. Which of the following is a *recent* event?
   (a) this morning's breakfast   (c) last night's supper
   (b) your grandparents' wedding   (d) your first day at school

2. Which of the following is *fragile*?
   (a) a baseball bat   (c) a gold ring
   (b) a glass ornament   (d) a tree limb

3. Which of the following might cause *concern*?
   (a) a toothache   (c) a hurricane warning
   (b) rising prices   (d) a furious customer

4. Which of the following could be a *menace* to drivers?
    (a) icy roads   (c) speed limits
    (b) thick fog   (d) seat belts

5. Which of the following might *pounce* on another animal?
    (a) an elephant   (c) a tiger
    (b) an eagle   (d) a mouse

6. Which of the following is a *symbol* of the United States?
    (a) the stars and stripes   (c) the bald eagle
    (b) the Statue of Liberty   (d) the Liberty Bell

7. For which of the following might you be given a *trophy*?
    (a) taking care of a little sister   (c) catching the biggest fish
    (b) winning a tennis match   (d) catching a cold

8. Which of the following might do *widespread* damage?
    (a) a flood   (c) a leaky roof
    (b) a hurricane   (d) an earthquake

15D Completing the Thought

Read each sentence below and fill in the blank with the correct word (or a form of the word) from the word list.

1. You need to add just a drop or two of that peppermint flavoring to the frosting. It is very _____.

2. Instead of strong blacks and clear whites, the photograph has only shades of gray. It lacks _____.

3. Smallpox is a disease that has now been completely wiped out. It used to be _____ , however.

4. I like that store because when I return something by mail, I get my money back immediately. They are very _____.

5. Although Marco's baby brother couldn't talk, when he saw Marco he clapped his hands and grinned. His delight was _____.

6. The park police will allow skating on the pond after three days of below-freezing temperatures. Then it will be _____ safe.

apparent
ban
concentrate
concern
consider
contrast
menace
prompt
talon
widespread

7. The town no longer allows people to park on downtown streets during rush hour. A _____ on parking is in effect.

8. The huge increase in the number of gypsy moths has us worried because we know how destructive they can be to trees. They are a _____.

9. When my brother Tony was late coming home from school, my father was worried. My mother said Tony was very responsible, though, so she wasn't _____.

10. The person who was in charge of birds at the zoo was especially careful in the hawk's cage. A hawk's _____ are very sharp.

15E Narrative

Read the narrative below; then complete the exercise that follows.

THE FALL AND RISE OF THE BALD EAGLE

For over two hundred years the bald eagle has been the **symbol** of America, with the likeness of this powerful bird found on our coins and on the Great Seal of the United States. Two hundred years ago, bald eagles were found throughout North America, but by the 1970s there were very few left outside of Alaska. The only creatures that **menace** the bald eagle are human beings. Why are there so few of these birds left? What are they like?

The bald eagle is a large, powerful bird that is not really bald. It gets its name from its white-feathered head, which **contrasts** strongly with the rest of its brown-feathered body. When it flies, it looks strong, powerful, and as if it is a master of the air. Its keen vision, great **talons**, and large, strongly hooked beak equip the bald eagle to live by hunting. In its search for small animals and fish, which form the greater part of its diet, it will sometimes **pounce** on a small lamb or piglet. Because of this, ranchers and farmers waged war on bald eagles for hundreds of years, killing them in large numbers. In addition, hunters shot them in order to have them stuffed as **trophies**.

In the 1950s it became **apparent** that there was a sharp drop in the number of bald eagles. The reason for this was soon discovered. The eagles' eggs were **fragile** and broke easily, killing the young chicks inside. The cause of the thin shells remained unknown for a number of years. Finally, the mystery was solved by a scientist named Rachel Carson.

Rachel Carson was **concerned** about the use of pesticides, chemicals used to kill insects that damage crops. In 1962 she wrote a book called *Silent Spring* that showed how some chemicals were harming the nation's wildlife. The book explained the cause of the thin eagle shells: it was DDT, a pesticide that had been in **widespread** use in the United States for over ten years. DDT had become **concentrated** in lakes and streams. Once it was in the water, it poisoned fish. The DDT in the fish that the bald eagles ate caused the birds to lay eggs that had the thinner shells that broke so easily.

Rachel Carson hoped that Congress would act **promptly** to end the use of DDT and save the national bird. But it was not until 1973 that Congress passed a law **banning** the use of DDT. In the same year it also passed a law that made it a crime to harm certain birds and animals, including the bald eagle, that were **considered** to be in danger.

In **recent** years these graceful and proud-looking birds have been observed in increasing numbers. A careful count made in 1994 revealed that there were about four thousand pairs of bald eagles in the United States. In that same year, the bald eagle was removed from the list of animals and birds in danger of dying out. The bald eagle had been given a chance to come back.

Answer each of the following questions in a sentence. If a question does not contain a vocabulary word, use a vocabulary word in your answer. Use each word only once. Questions and answers will then contain all fifteen words (or forms of the words) from this lesson's word list.

1. When would a farmer be most likely to kill a bald eagle?

   _____

2. When did we find out that the bald eagle was in danger of dying out?

   _____

3. What was the reason for the drop in the number of bald eagles?

   _____

4. Explain why this story of the bald eagle has a happy ending.

   _____

5. Why did the bald eagle have good reason to fear human beings?

   _____

6. How does the bald eagle capture its food?

   _____

7. How did Rachel Carson show her **concern** about what was happening to the nation's wildlife?

   _____

8. What happened to DDT after it had been sprayed on crops?

   _____

9. Where was DDT used?

   _____

10. What did some hunters do with the bald eagles they shot?

    _____

11. What is the meaning of **considered** as it is used in the narrative?

    _____

12. Why was it important for Congress to act **promptly**?

    _____

13. What did Congress finally do?

    _____

14. How did the bald eagle get its name?

    _____

15. Why does a picture of the bald eagle appear on the Great Seal of the United States?

    _____

WORDLY WISE

When the Apollo astronauts returned to earth, they brought back *fragments* of rocks from the moon. The word means "parts that are broken off," and comes from the Latin *fractus*, which means "broken." Several other English words are formed from this same Latin root. If you break a bone, you have a *fracture*. If you break down the number 1 into smaller parts, such as halves or quarters, you get *fractions*. Finally, something that is **fragile** is easily broken.

When a stage actor forgets the next line, which is every actor's nightmare, a person off to the side may **prompt** him or her by saying it aloud. The *prompter* must say the line loud enough for the actor to hear but not so loud that the audience hears. If the audience does hear the prompter, the play usually gets an unintended laugh.

A *cymbal* is a musical instrument; it is one of a pair of brass plates that are struck together to make a ringing sound. This word and **symbol** are homonyms, words that sound alike but have different meanings and different spellings.

Lesson 16

Word List

Study the definitions of the words below; then do the exercises for the lesson.

apt
adj. 1. Suited to; fitting.
["The Stilts" was an *apt* nickname for seven-foot-one-inch basketball star Wilt Chamberlain.]
2. Likely or almost certain.
[I am *apt* to do better on Spanish tests if I make vocabulary cards to study.]

blossom
n. A flower.
[The white orange *blossom* stands out against the dark-green foliage.]
v. 1. To come into bloom.
[Dogwood trees *blossom* in May.]
2. To develop.
[After two years of playing bit parts, she *blossomed* into a star of the Broadway stage.]

bough
n. A large branch or limb of a tree.
[The *boughs* of the apple tree were heavy with fruit.]

content
adj. Happy with what one has; satisfied.
[Give me a good book and a comfortable armchair and I am *content*.]
contentment *n.* A state of being satisfied and at peace.
[After a delicious dinner and a hot bath, I relaxed in total *contentment*.]

detest
v. To dislike strongly; to hate.
[Many Germans *detested* Hitler, but were afraid to speak out.]
detestable *adj.* Causing or deserving strong dislike.
[His racist views are *detestable,* but in a free society he has a right to express them.]

dusk
n. The time at the end of the day just before dark.
[The streetlights go on at *dusk*.]

extinguish
v. 1. To put out, as a fire or a light.
[The sign at the campsite said, "Before leaving, make sure you *extinguish* your campfire."]

familiar
adj. 1. Often seen or experienced; known.
[I was happy to see a *familiar* face in the crowd.]
2. Having a good knowledge of.
[Dan read about it in the newspaper and is *familiar* with the case.]

obtain
v. To gain or get by making an effort.
[We were lucky to *obtain* tickets for the jazz concert because they sold out very quickly.]

orchard
n. A place where fruit trees grow.
[Every fall my brother and I go to an *orchard* where you can pick your own apples.]

practice   *v.* 1. To say or do over and over.
[If you *practice* Spanish every day, you should be able to get along when you go to Mexico.]
2. To do; carry on, perform.
[He was raised from an early age to *practice* politeness.]
3. To work at as a profession.
[Aunt Marianna is licensed to *practice* law in both California and Nevada.]
n. 1. A repeated action or usual way of doing something.
[It's my mother's *practice* to swim thirty laps every morning.]
2. The work of a profession.
[The *practice* of medicine has recently undergone many changes.]

prune   *v.* To cut off branches.
[We had to *prune* the shrubs so we could see out of the window.]
n. A dried plum.
[Elijah usually soaks the *prunes* overnight and serves them for breakfast.]

stout   *adj.* 1. Heavily built; thickset.
[He used to be thin, but he grew *stout* as he got older.]
2. Strong; not easily bent or broken.
[The roof of the barn was supported by six *stout* posts.]

threadbare   *adj.* Shabby and worn-out.
[The *threadbare* blankets on the bed failed to keep us warm during the night.]

wander   *v.* 1. To go from place to place with no plan or purpose in mind.
[We *wandered* around downtown, waiting for the post office to open.]
2. To slip easily off the subject; to fail to work in a normal way.
[Luis tried to concentrate on his math homework, but his mind began to *wander*.]

16A Finding Meanings

Choose two phrases to form a sentence that correctly uses a word from Word List 16. Write each sentence in the space provided.

1. (a) A blossom is
   (b) A practice is
   (c) the work of a profession.
   (d) something that is done right the first time.

_____

2. (a) A familiar person is one who is
   (b) A stout person is one who is
   (c) a close relative.
   (d) heavily built.

_____

3. (a) To extinguish a light is to
   (b) To obtain a light is to
   (c) put it out.
   (d) put a shade over it.

_____

4. (a) To prune is to   (c) gather fruit.
   (b) travel aimlessly.   (d) To wander is to

---

5. (a) whatever is inside something.   (c) Contentment is
   (b) the approach of darkness.   (d) Dusk is

---

6. (a) An orchard is   (c) a flower.
   (b) A blossom is   (d) a piece of fruit.

---

7. (a) is found after a search.   (c) Something that is detestable
   (b) Something that is apt   (d) deserves hate.

---

8. (a) get rid of it.   (c) To practice something is to
   (b) keep doing it.   (d) To obtain something is to

---

9. (a) a type of dried fruit.   (c) A bough is
   (b) a place where fruit grows.   (d) A prune is

16B Just the Right Word

Improve each of the following sentences by crossing out the italicized phrase and replacing it with a word (or a form of the word) from Word List 16.

1. I *strongly dislike* your taste in music.

2. As I crawled along the *branch of the tree*, it began to bend under my weight.

3. If I raise my grade to a B-plus, I will be *very satisfied*.

4. After three nights without enough sleep, my mind began to *fail to work in a normal way*.

5. My cousin's farm includes a large *piece of land on which fruit trees are growing*.

6. My favorite blue sweater is *shabby and worn out,* but I refuse to throw it away.

7. My piano teacher said that if I keep *playing that part over and over again,* I'll have the whole piece memorized.

8. Beginning skiers are *very likely* to fall many times while they are learning.

9. Gina is going to *get hold of* the equipment we need for the camping trip.

10. Your face is *known to me,* but I can't remember your name.

11. When do the rose bushes start to *have flowers growing on them?*

16C Applying Meanings

Circle the letter of each correct answer to the questions below. A question may have more than one correct answer.

1. Which of the following might be *stout?*
   (a) a person
   (b) a rope
   (c) a walking stick
   (d) a cobweb

2. Which of the following would grow in an *orchard?*
   (a) pears
   (b) peaches
   (c) potatoes
   (d) tomatoes

3. Which of the following happens at *dusk?*
   (a) the stars begin to appear
   (b) it gets darker
   (c) the sun rises
   (d) it gets cloudy

4. Which of the following can a person *obtain?*
   (a) a car roof rack
   (b) a car trip
   (c) a phone number
   (d) a phone call

5. Which of the following can be *pruned?*
   (a) trees
   (b) leaves
   (c) roots
   (d) branches

6. Which of the following might bring you *contentment?*
   (a) being with your family
   (b) getting together with friends
   (c) feeling concerned about your health
   (d) missing an important date

7. Which of the following are *familiar* sights in the city?
   (a) buses
   (b) taxicabs
   (c) shoppers
   (d) police cars

8. Which of the following might *wander*?

    (a) a train   (c) a person going for a long walk

    (b) a lost child   (d) a person setting off for work

16D Completing the Thought

Read each sentence below and fill in the blank with the correct word (or a form of the word) from the word list.

| apt |
| blossom |
| bough |
| content |
| extinguish |
| familiar |
| practice |
| prune |
| threadbare |
| wander |

1. The room was plunged into darkness when a sudden gust of wind blew out the candle. It _____ the light.

2. Charlie Chaplin played a tramp in so many movies that he was called The Little Tramp. The name was quite _____.

3. Joe's shirt had been washed so many times that it had worn quite thin; you could almost see through it. It was _____.

4. Manu loved climbing on the lowest branch of the oak tree. The _____ was just the right height for him.

5. Ramona, who has been weaving baskets since she was a child, explained that it is an art that is thousands of years old. She _____ an ancient craft.

6. I thought there was no one I knew at the party, but then I heard a voice that sounded like that of my old roommate. The voice sounded very _____.

7. After a shaky start, Sergei's career suddenly took off, and he rapidly became one of the world's best ballet dancers. He _____ into an expert dancer.

8. Paloma explained that cutting away some of the branches would give the tree more light, and it would be healthier as a result. She was going to _____ it.

9. When we go on a trip, Raoul hates to follow a map. He'd rather just _____.

10. Henry loved his family, his job, and his garden. He was _____.

16E Narrative

Read the narrative below; then complete the exercise that follows.

THE STORY OF JOHNNY APPLESEED

In the late 1700s, most Americans had never tasted an apple. That's because very few apple trees grew outside of New England. A man named John Chapman did more than anyone else to change that. He enjoyed sinking his teeth into a sweet, juicy apple and wanted to share his enjoyment with others. For forty years, as he **wandered** through Ohio, Indiana, and western Pennsylvania, it was his **practice** to take a bag of apple seeds with him, planting them as he went along.

Chapman **obtained** the seeds from New England cider mills after the apples had been pressed for cider. Over the years, due entirely to his efforts, apple **orchards** were growing in many of the places he had visited. From time to time, he returned to them in order to **prune** the trees and make sure they stayed healthy.

This unusual man was born in Leominster, Massachusetts, and began his travels in 1797, when he was in his early twenties. When he needed money, he knew that just down the road there would be someone who would give him work and pay him a dollar or two. Chapman spent most days on the road, a **stout** walking stick cut from an apple tree in his hand and a tall, black hat on his head. At **dusk,** he looked for a place to spend the night. If there was no house with a room to offer him near-by, he was **content** to sleep under the stars. He had few needs, and it didn't bother him that his clothes were **threadbare.**

Because he **detested** killing of any kind, John Chapman refused to eat meat. Once he even **extinguished** a campfire because mosquitoes were flying into the flames and dying. He had no fear of wild animals, and they seemed to sense that he would do them no harm. In one of the many stories told about Chapman, he spent the night in the company of a friendly bear.

When he returned to places he had visited before, Chapman was greeted as an old friend. He loved to come back in the spring and see apple trees he had planted years before full of pink and white **blossoms.** But his greatest pleasure was to return in the fall to see their **boughs** weighed down with apples. Over the years he became a **familiar** sight to the people living on the farms and in the small towns of the Ohio River Valley. They gave him the very **apt** name we know him by today—Johnny Appleseed.

Answer each of the following questions in a sentence. If a question does not contain a vocabulary word, use a vocabulary word in your answer. Use each word only once. Questions and answers will then contain all fifteen words (or forms of the words) from this lesson's word list.

1. Why is Johnny Appleseed an **apt** name for John Chapman?

    _____

2. Why did people have reason to be grateful to Chapman?

    _____

3. How do we know Chapman was not vain about his appearance?

    _____

4. Why did Chapman refuse to eat meat?

    _____

5. How can we tell that John Chapman was not usually in a hurry?

    _____

6. What is the meaning of **practice** as it is used in the narrative?

    _____

7. Where did Chapman get his apple seeds?

    _____

8. What did Chapman look for in choosing something from which to make a walking stick?

    _____

9. What did Chapman do at the end of the day when he was traveling?

    _____

10. What did Chapman do if there was no one to give him a night's lodging?

    _____

11. Why did Chapman once put out his campfire?

    _____

12. What sight did Chapman enjoy in the spring?

    _____

13. Did the apple trees Chapman planted yield much fruit?

_____

14. How do you know that Chapman often returned to places he had been to before?

_____

15. Why did Chapman return to places where he had planted trees?

_____

WORDLY WISE

In Lesson 10 you learned that the word *orphan* comes from an old Sanskrit word. Another word that comes from this same language is **apt.** The Sanskrit word *apta* means "suitable" or "fitting." An *apt* remark is one that is a suitable or fitting thing to say.

In some languages, such as Russian, a word is pronounced the way it is spelled. That is not the case with English, which is one of the reasons English can be so difficult to learn. The word **bough,** for example, rhymes with *cow.* Imagine a person studying English who learns this and then tries to read the following sentences, all of which contain words ending in *-ough*:

I have a bad *cough* (rhymes with *off*). I've had *enough* (rhymes with *stuff*). I'm coming *through* (rhymes with *shoe*). Bread is made from *dough* (rhymes with *go*).

As an adjective, **content** means "satisfied." It can also be a noun, however, meaning "the amount contained." Then it is pronounced 'con tent. (Water with a high lead *content* is unfit to drink.) The word is often used in its plural form, *contents*, and means "all that is contained." (The grocery bag split, spilling its *contents* onto the floor.)

CROSSWORD PUZZLE

Solve the crossword puzzle below by studying the clues and filling in the answer boxes. Clues followed by a number are definitions of words in Lessons 13—16. The number gives the word list in which the answer to the clue appears.

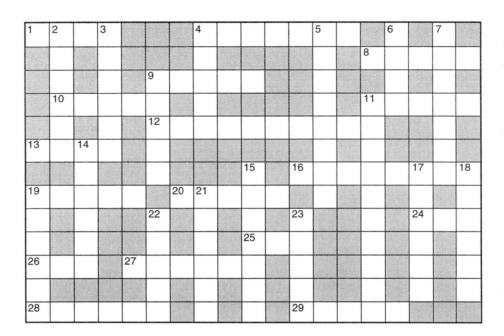

Clues Across

1. To defeat completely (13)
4. To believe without having proof (13)
8. To have and take pride in (14)
9. Several notes of music played together (14)
10. To cause horror, shock, or dismay (13)
11. Chairs go around it.
12. To put out, as a fire or a light (16)
13. Short for "Andrew"
16. In low spirits (13)
19. To beg; to ask for something (14)
20. The claw of a bird that hunts small animals (15)
24. Suited to; fitting (16)
25. One, _____ , three
26. April, _____ , June
27. Not proud; modest (14)
28. To walk slowly and heavily (14)
29. It comes from bees.

Clues Down

2. To get by making an effort (16)
3. A prize or award (15)
4. Strong; not easily bent or broken (16)
5. To give careful thought to (15)
6. A state in the Midwest
7. To set apart (13)
9. Opposite of "dirty"
11. Shabby; worn out (16)
14. Lacking fun or excitement (13)
15. Satisfied with what one has (16)
17. Causing great sadness (13)
18. To dislike strongly (16)
19. Quick; without too much time passing (15)
21. Saudi _____ , a country in the Middle East
22. To cut off parts, especially branches (16)
23. A large branch of a tree (16)

Lesson 17

Word List

Study the definitions of the words below; then do the exercises for the lesson.

address
v. 1. (uh 'dress) To direct one's words to.
[The head of the honor society *addressed* the whole student body.]
2. To apply oneself to something.
[As soon as Ms. Lu finishes solving one problem, she has to *address* a new one.]
n. 1. A written or spoken speech.
[President Lincoln scribbled the Gettysbury *Address* on an envelope.]
2. ('a dres) The place where someone lives or receives mail.
[Let the post office know if you change your *address*.]

approve
v. To think well of; to agree to.
[My friend Lucia *approved* my choice of a dress for the party.]
approval *n.* Thinking well of; agreeing to.
[My parents' *approval* is important to me.]

conclude
v. 1. To bring or come to an end.
[It took us at least ten minutes to reach the exit after the concert *concluded*.]
2. To form an opinion.
[Jan *concluded* that mowing lawns was the best way to earn money next summer.]
conclusion *n.* 1. The end.
[A bow by the conductor marked the *conclusion* of the concert.]
2. A judgment.
[After talking to my teachers and my parents I came to the *conclusion* that taking Spanish would be more useful to me than French.]

deprive
v. To keep from having; to take away from.
[The thunderstorm at 3:00 a.m. *deprived* me of a good night's sleep.]

elder
n. 1. A person who is older.
[Sometimes we can learn a lot from our *elders* just by observing the way they live their lives.]
2. Someone people look up to because of age and experience.
[The *elders* of the village met to decide what to do about the increasing number of tourists.]
adj. Older.
[My *elder* brother is a senior in high school.]

escort
v. To travel with; to guide or protect a person.
[In our neighborhood a parent or friend always *escorts* a child to kindergarten.]
n. One or more persons that escort.
[The president always has a police *escort* from the airport to the White House.]

fare
n. 1. Money paid for a trip, by bus or train, for example.
[What is the *fare* from Chicago to Orlando by air?]
2. Food and drink.
[The new restaurant serves Chinese *fare*.]
v. To get along.
[I wonder how my sister is *faring* on her mountain climbing trip.]

forlorn   *adj.* Sad and lonely.
[Sam looked lost and *forlorn* as he sat waiting for his mother.]

hearty   *adj.* 1. Healthy; strong.
[All the runners were *hearty* and expected to finish the race in record time.]
2. Large and satisfying.
[The *hearty* vegetable chili hit the spot on a cold day.]
3. Friendly and enthusiastic.
[Santa gave a *hearty* "Ho, ho, ho" when my little brother climbed onto his knee.]

inhale   *v.* To breathe in.
[I tried to catch my breath by *inhaling* deeply several times.]

merit   *v.* To deserve.
[The students' ideas for changes in the sports program *merit* careful study by the school board.]
n. Good qualities; worth.
[Dalal's teacher thought his fund-raising idea had *merit* and asked him to explain it to the class.]
merits   *n. pl.* The actual facts.
[The judge said to forget what we'd heard on television and judge the case on its *merits*.]

stingy   *adj.* Not generous.
[Azania is too *stingy* to share her candy with anyone.]

summon   *v.* 1. To call or send for.
[My father *summoned* me to the phone.]
2. To call forth; to gather.
[I *summoned* all my courage and walked out on the stage.]

valiant   *adj.* Full of courage; brave.
[The patriots were honored for their *valiant* deeds.]

waft   *v.* To move or be moved lightly over water or air; to drift.
[Petals from the cherry blossoms *wafted* over the path on the gentle breeze.]

17A Finding Meanings

Choose two phrases to form a sentence that correctly uses a word from Word List 17. Write each sentence in the space provided.

1. (a) An address is
   (b) A fare is
   (c) the time spent alone.
   (d) the money charged for a trip.

   _____

2. (a) breathe it in.
   (b) do without it.
   (c) To conclude something is to
   (d) To inhale something is to

   _____

3. (a) one that is enthusiastic.   (c) A forlorn expression is
   (b) one that shows agreement.   (d) A hearty laugh is

4. (a) The conclusion of a play is   (c) the beginning of it.
   (b) The merit of a play is   (d) the end of it.

5. (a) decide against it.   (c) To approve something is to
   (b) ask that person to come.   (d) To summon someone is to

6. (a) to be worthy of it.   (c) To deprive of praise is
   (b) To merit praise is   (d) to value it.

7. (a) A person's approval is   (c) A person's address is
   (b) the place he lives.   (d) a feeling of distrust.

8. (a) Someone who is forlorn   (c) feels good about the future.
   (b) Someone who is valiant   (d) feels sad and lonely.

9. (a) a business partner.   (c) a wise, old person.
   (b) An escort is   (d) An elder is

10. (a) A stingy person is   (c) one who is full of courage.
    (b) A valiant person is   (d) one who is generous.

17B Just the Right Word

Improve each of the following sentences by crossing out the italicized phrase and replacing it with a word (or a form of the word) from Word List 17.

1. The smell of freshly-mown hay *was carried by the breeze* across the meadow.

2. Trees that are *prevented from getting a supply* of proper nourishment will die.

3. The New Town Inn boasts that it offers the finest *food and drink* at the lowest prices in town.

4. My *view, after thinking about all the issues,* is that no real harm was done.

5. "Allow me to *stay beside you and walk with* you to your carriage," the gatekeeper said.

6. Samantha cannot marry without her parents' *agreement that she is doing the right thing.*

7. After such a *large and satisfying* meal, we all felt like taking naps.

8. They are so *unwilling to spend any more than they absolutely have to* that they expect me to babysit for fifty cents an hour.

9. The lawyer said that as long as the case is decided on the *facts as they are known,* her client will win.

10. Mayor Menino *made a few remarks to* the people gathered outside City Hall, thanking them for their support.

17C Applying Meanings

Circle the letter of each correct answer to the questions below. A question may have more than one correct answer.

1. Which of the following can be concluded?
   (a) a speech
   (b) an agreement
   (c) a meeting
   (d) a thought

2. Which of the following can waft?
   (a) smoke
   (b) smells
   (c) rain
   (d) leaves

3. Which of the following can be hearty?
   (a) a meal   (c) a storm
   (b) a greeting   (d) an appetite

4. Which of the following show approval?
   (a) turning thumbs down   (c) cheering
   (b) applauding   (d) booing

5. Which of the following is a valiant act?
   (a) giving up easily   (c) running away
   (b) standing up for one's beliefs   (d) blaming someone else

6. Of which of the following can one be deprived?
   (a) one's freedom   (c) one's good name
   (b) one's rights   (d) one's business

7. Which of the following can be addressed?
   (a) a meeting   (c) a package
   (b) a person   (d) a nation

8. Which of the following can be inhaled?
   (a) air   (c) smoke
   (b) food   (d) music

17D Completing the Thought

Read each sentence below and fill in the blank with the correct word (or a form of the word) from the word list.

1. The puppy was shivering with cold and looked as though it were lost and hadn't eaten for some time. It looked utterly _____.

2. Carlos and Juanita are twins, but Juanita was born ten minutes before her brother. She is the _____ of the two.

3. Bill's suggestion that they open a smaller store and make him manager was an idea the owners liked. They thought it had a great deal of _____.

4. Although the check for dinner came to thirty-four dollars, Mr. Wickman left only a dollar on the table as a tip for the server. Everyone knew he was very _____.

address
approve
elder
escort
fare
forlorn
merit
stingy
summon
valiant

5. The juniors always rang the big bell to tell people graduation was about to begin. It was a nice way to _____ people.

6. The governor's message will be broadcast by all the television networks at eight o'clock. It will be his annual _____.

7. I love pad thai, jasmine rice, and shrimp curry. Thai food is my favorite restaurant _____.

8. Kitty decided not to go to the dance alone, so she asked Roger to go with her. She wanted an _____.

9. Doctors cannot prescribe a medicine until the government has tested it. New medicines must be _____ first.

10. In spite of the fact that Oscar was seriously ill, he went to work every day, never complained, and was generally cheerful. We all admired him for being so _____.

17E Narrative

Read the narrative below; then complete the exercise that follows.

AN AFRICAN FOLK TALE

Some folk tales tell of **valiant** deeds performed by great heroes; an example is the Japanese story of Tokoyo and the sea monster. Others, like the Welsh tale of the silver cows and the water lilies, explain how things came to be. A third group tells how the weak and helpless defeat the strong and powerful. This does not always happen in real life, but it does happen in folk tales, as in this East African story of the *maskini* and the *tajiri*.

Every evening, the *tajiri*, or rich man, sat down to a **hearty** meal prepared for him in his own kitchen. The food that was left over would have been enough to feed a whole family, but the *tajiri* was extremely **stingy**. The leftovers from his table went to fatten his pigs so that he would have the benefit of them later.

The *maskini*, or poor man, lived on simple **fare**. He owned a goat that gave him milk and cheese, but his evening meal was usually nothing more than a bowl of porridge. However, he had found a way to make it more enjoyable. He would eat his meal while hidden outside the *tajiri*'s kitchen, where wonderful smells came **wafting** through the open window. They made the *maskini*'s mouth water, and the porridge seemed like a feast.

One evening, the *tajiri* decided to take a walk in his garden in order to work up an appetite for dinner. He saw the *maskini* sitting outside the kitchen window. As the *tajiri* watched, he saw the *maskini* **inhale** deeply, and a blissful look come over his face. How dare he help himself to my smells, thought the *tajiri,* and he ordered his servants to seize the *maskini* and **escort** him to the village jail.

A few days later, the *maskini* was **summoned** before the court that met weekly in the village center, where the case would be decided on its **merits.** The *tajiri* explained that the smells from the kitchen belonged to him, and the *maskini* was **depriving** him of them. As payment, he demanded the *maskini's* goat, which was the only thing he owned. When asked to respond, the *maskini,* looking very **forlorn,** could only stare at the ground and shuffle his feet, afraid to speak. The village **elders,** who had been hearing the case, now withdrew to the shade of a nearby baobab tree. After a brief discussion, the village chief came forward and **addressed** the crowd.

"The *maskini* did help himself to the smells from the *tajiri's* kitchen," she said. "However, he did not receive any food from him. We have **concluded,** therefore, that the *tajiri* should not be given the goat. However, in fairness to him we believe he should have the right to smell the *maskini's* goat whenever he wants."

The *tajiri* was furious and left without saying a word. But the people of the village **approved** the court's decision. They felt that justice had been done.

Answer each of the following questions in a sentence. If a question does not contain a vocabulary word, use a vocabulary word in your answer. Use each word only once. Questions and answers will then contain all fifteen words (or forms of the words) from this lesson's word list.

1. Did the *maskini* put up a **valiant** defense in the court?

_____

2. What is the meaning of **hearty** as it is used in the narrative?

_____

3. The story says the *tajiri* was **stingy.** How does it show this?

_____

4. How did the *tajiri* **fare** when he went to court?

_____

5. What would have happened if the kitchen window had been closed?

_____

6. How did the *tajiri* know that the *maskini* was enjoying the smells from the kitchen?

_____

7. Why did the *maskini* need an **escort**?

_____

8. Did the *maskini* have to go to court?

_____

9. What does it mean to say the case would be decided on its **merits**?

_____

10. Had the *maskini* taken anything from the *tajiri?*

_____

11. Why do you think the *maskini* looked **forlorn**?

_____

12. What sort of person might become one of the village **elders**?

_____

13. To whom did the chief direct her remarks?

_____

14 What is the meaning of **concluded** as it is used in the narrative?

_____

15. How might the crowd have shown that it **approved** of the court's decision?

_____

WORDLY WISE

President Lincoln gave a famous speech at Gettysburg in 1863 that begins, "Four score and seven years ago . . ." Why do we refer to it as the Gettysburg **Address** rather than the Gettysburg Speech? One reason is that *address* suggests something grander and more important than a speech. Anyone can make a speech, but you have to be someone important and the occasion a special one for it to be called an address.

As an adjective, **elder** means "great*er* than another in age or seniority." If we refer to someone great*est* in age or seniority, we use *eldest*. (I have an *elder* brother named Mark. He is not the *eldest*.) (Sheila is the *eldest* of seven children.) Note that *elder* and *eldest* are used only when referring to persons, but *older* and *oldest* can refer either to persons or things.

We turn many words into their opposites simply by changing the prefix. **Inhale** means "to breathe in." It is made up of the prefix *in-*, meaning "in" and the root formed from the Latin verb *halare*, meaning "to breathe." By knowing that the prefix *ex-* means "out," you can turn *inhale* into its opposite and make a word that means "to breathe out." What is that word?

Lesson 18

Word List

Study the definitions of the words below; then do the exercises for the lesson.

abreast   *adj.* or *adv.* 1. Side-by-side.
[We walked three *abreast,* except where the path was so narrow that we had to walk single file.]
2. Up-to-date.
[I try to stay *abreast* of what is happening in the world by reading the paper every day.]

barrier   *n.* Anything that stops progress or blocks the way.
[Lack of education is often a *barrier* to success in life.]

breadth   *n.* 1. The distance of something from side to side; width.
[The arrow missed the target by no more than a hand's *breadth*.]
2. Wide range; largeness.
[Carlos got the job because of his *breadth* of experience.]

capital   *n.* 1. Wealth that can be used to produce more wealth.
[You don't need much *capital* to buy that pizza business.]
2. The city where the government of a state or country is located.
[The *capital* of Montana is Helena.]
adj. Punishable by death.
[Murder is a *capital* crime in many states.]

ensure   *v.* To make sure or certain.
[Wearing a seat belt will help *ensure* your safety in case of an accident.]

external   *adj.* On or related to the outside.
[The *external* walls of the house are covered with shingles as protection.]

feud   *n.* A long, bitter quarrel, especially one between two families.
[It took the tragic deaths of Romeo and Juliet to end the *feud* between their two families.]
v. To be enemies, to quarrel.
[The Hatfields and the McCoys *feuded* for years.]

fortress   *n.* A building with strong walls made to be defended against attack; a fort.
[Rather than attack the *fortress* directly, the invaders went around it.]

frequent   *adj.* Happening often or over and over.
[My mother's business requires her to make *frequent* visits to Japan.]
v. To go to over and over.
[We *frequent* the local bakery regularly for oatmeal cookies.]
frequency *n.* Number of times something is repeated.
[My clarinet playing improved with the *frequency* of my practicing.]

frontier   *n.* 1. The line between two countries.
[We said goodbye to France and crossed the *frontier* into Spain in the early morning.]
2. The outer limits of the settled part of a country.
[The American *frontier* moved slowly westward in the nineteenth century.]
3. The outer limits of knowledge.
[The *frontiers* of medicine are being pushed back at a rapidly increasing rate.]

peasant   *n.* A person who makes a living from working the soil, especially in poorer countries.
[The *peasant's* revolt in England in 1381 was a shock to the government.]

petty   *adj.* 1. Of little importance; small.
[A *petty* disagreement over a parking space was the beginning of their long-lasting feud.]

threat   n. A warning that one may do harm.
[Olivia tried to quiet her dog after her neighbor's *threat* to call the police.]
threaten   *v.* To make a threat.
[My brother *threatened* to tell my mother that I ate all the cake.]
threatening   *adj.* Suggesting harm or danger.
[The dark clouds looked very *threatening*.]

utilize   *v.* To put to use.
[We *utilized* whatever scraps of fabric we had to make a Halloween costume.]

vast   *adj.* Very great in area or amount.
[The Pacific Ocean is a *vast* body of water.]

18A Finding Meanings

Choose two phrases to form a sentence that correctly uses a word from Word List 18. Write each sentence in the space provided.

1. (a) The breadth of something is
   (b) the number of times it occurs.
   (c) The frequency of something is
   (d) its unexpected absence.

2. (a) A frontier is
   (b) A barrier is
   (c) a person who makes a living from the soil.
   (d) the outer limits of the settled part of a country.

3. (a) Capital is
   (b) severe punishment.
   (c) Breadth is
   (d) distance from side to side.

4. (a) to have knowledge of it.
   (b) to avoid it.
   (c) To be abreast of something is
   (d) To ensure something is

5. (a) is punishable by death.   (c) A petty crime is one that
  (b) goes unpunished.   (d) A capital crime is one that

6. (a) something that blocks the way.   (c) A peasant is
  (b) something that can be used.   (d) A barrier is

7. (a) A vast army   (c) is one that has been routed.
  (b) is one about to attack.   (d) A threatening army

8. (a) A fortress is   (c) a person who makes a living from the soil.
  (b) A peasant is   (d) a humble cottage.

9. (a) A petty difference is   (c) one that keeps increasing.
  (b) one of little importance.   (d) A vast difference is

10. (a) A fortress is   (c) A feud is
  (b) a bitter quarrel.   (d) the line between two countries.

11. (a) make sure it happens.   (c) To ensure something is to
  (b) make sure it doesn't happen.   (d) To utilize something is to

18B Just the Right Word

Improve each of the following sentences by crossing out the italicized phrase and replacing it with a word (or a form of the word) from Word List 18.

1. My father *puts to good use* every leftover when he makes a casserole.

2. A *building that is made to be defended against attack* should be built on high ground.

3. A country needs *wealth that can be used to produce more wealth* in order to produce jobs.

4. The points Eric raised were so *lacking in importance* that everyone ignored them.

5. If you try to *suggest that you could be a danger to* me, I won't talk to you any more.

6. I know most of the people who *make regular visits to* the Cosy Cafe; I have lunch there every day.

7. Most streets aren't wide enough for three cyclists riding *side by side.*

8. The land of the former Soviet Union is so *great in the area it covers* that it crosses nine time zones.

9. The first symptoms of measles are *on the outside.*

10. Many of the *lines separating the various countries* of Europe were redrawn after the First World War.

11. The two families continued to *keep up the long and bitter quarrel* because neither side was willing to give in.

18C Applying Meanings

Circle the letter of each correct answer to the questions below. A question may have more than one correct answer.

1. Which of the following has *breadth?*
    (a) a table top
    (b) a point where lines meet
    (c) a brick
    (d) a line joining two points

2. Which of the following is an *external* symptom?
    (a) a sore throat
    (b) a stomach ache
    (c) a skin rash
    (d) a twitching eyelid

3. In which of the following places are you likely to find a *peasant?*
    (a) a city
    (b) a farm
    (c) an office
    (d) a field

4. Which of the following is a *threatening* remark?
    (a) "See you later."
    (b) "I'll get even with you!"
    (c) "You'll be sorry."
    (d) "I'm sorry."

5. Which of the following would be considered *vast?*
    (a) the Atlantic Ocean
    (b) the distance to the nearest star
    (c) the universe
    (d) the American prairie

6. Which of the following is a *capital?*
   - (a) Washington, D.C.
   - (b) Paris, France
   - (c) Ottawa, Canada
   - (d) Bronx, New York

7. Which of the following are *petty* concerns?
   - (a) your choice of breakfast cereal
   - (b) your choice of school
   - (c) a broken fingernail
   - (d) a broken leg

8. Which of the following do people change *frequently?*
   - (a) their date of birth
   - (b) their socks
   - (c) their eating habits
   - (d) their names

18D Completing the Thought

Read each sentence below and fill in the blank with the correct word (or a form of the word) from the word list.

1. The bus downtown used to go every half hour, but now it goes every fifteen minutes. I'm really glad it's more _____.

2. Moira's refrigerator is full of small containers of leftovers. Her family _____ every scrap for their tasty meals.

3. The Flying Wallabies are great trapeze artists, but even they do not perform unless there is a net beneath them. The net is there to _____ their safety.

4. The men were protected on all sides behind the twenty-foot walls, so Gurdred decided it was useless to attack. He had to think of another way to get into the _____.

5. Perry's dog, George, barks a lot and jumps up on you, but he is really quite harmless. He is not a _____ to anyone.

6. We know a great deal about our own planet, but we have a lot to learn about what goes on in outer space. Space is the new _____.

7. While my little brother and his friend kept arguing about what flavor ice cream to get, I was reading a mystery. I hate _____ arguments.

8. Workers set up fences to keep people away from the film crew, who were making a movie. We were not allowed to cross the _____.

barrier
ensure
feud
fortress
frequent
frontier
petty
threat
utilize

9. The quarrel between the two families had been going on for such a long time that no one could recall how it had begun. It was a mysterious _____.

18E Narrative

Read the narrative below; then complete the exercise that follows.

THE GREAT WALL OF CHINA

Most visitors to China make a point of seeing the Great Wall. It is hard to miss because of its enormous size. It is about twenty-five feet high, and its **breadth** at the top is nearly twenty feet, wide enough for ten people to walk **abreast**. It starts in Gansu province in the south and ends at the Yellow Sea in the northeast, a distance of fifteen hundred miles. The part of the wall tourists visit most **frequently** goes from Beijing, the **capital** of China, to the Yellow Sea.

The Great Wall of China was built more than two thousand years ago as a **barrier** against tribes from the north. The person responsible for having it built was Shi Huang-ti, known as "the First Emperor of China." Before the country was united under his leadership, China was divided into a large number of **petty** kingdoms, ruled by local warlords who spent most of their time **feuding** among themselves. By the year 221 B.C., Shi Huang-ti had taken control of the whole country and made himself emperor.

Because the empire was so **vast**, it was not easy to defend. Shi Huang-ti had nothing to fear at home, but he worried about **external** attacks, especially from the north, where tribes from central Asia **threatened** his rule. To **ensure** the safety of his empire, he had the Great Wall built along China's northern **frontier**. It had watchtowers every few miles, as well as **fortresses** where the emperor's soldiers were housed, ready to fight off attacks. Building began in 214 B.C., and later rulers of China added to it in the west and south. Work on the wall was still being carried out four centuries ago.

Hundreds of thousands of Chinese **peasants** were forced to leave their farms to do the actual work of building the Great Wall. Everything had to be carried on the workers' backs or slung on poles because the wheelbarrow had not yet been invented. The builders **utilized** whatever was close at hand—blocks of stone in mountain areas and timber from forests. In other places they used earth or sand mixed with twigs and reeds. Later on, bricks and tiles were used.

Shi Huang-ti is an important figure in Chinese history. He improved the workings of government and ordered the building of roads and canals to improve communications throughout the empire. He built a magnificent palace as well as many other fine public buildings. But his greatest achievement, and the thing for which he is remembered, is the Great Wall of China.

Answer each of the following questions in a sentence. If a question does not contain a vocabulary word, use a vocabulary word in your answer. Use each word only once. Questions and answers will then contain all fifteen words (or forms of the words) from this lesson's word list.

1. Why do you think tourists visit the Great Wall so **frequently**?

   _____

2. Why does it take a very long time to cross China?

   _____

3. Why would you expect to find many government offices in Beijing?

   _____

4. Why did the "First Emperor" build the Great Wall?

   _____

5. What enemies was Shi Huang-ti worried about?

   _____

6. How did the local warlords get along with each other?

   _____

7. How much influence do you think the ruler of a **petty** kingdom would have?

   _____

8. Why was Shi Huang-ti concerned about the tribes in Central Asia?

   _____

9. Where would an invasion of China by the northern tribes have taken place?

   _____

10. What materials did the builders of the wall use?

   _____

11. What was the purpose of the **fortresses** that were built into the wall?

_____

12. Why was it possible to use the top of the Great Wall as a road?

_____

13. Why would the Great Wall be easy to see from the air?

_____

14. Why might the **peasants** have resented having to work on the wall?

_____

15. Was the Great Wall successful in doing what it was suppose to do?

_____

WORDLY WISE

Don't confuse the word **capital**, which has several meanings as an adjective and is also a noun, with the word *capitol,* which is a noun only.

The Capitol (with an upper-case C) is the building in which the United States Congress meets. A capitol (with a lower case *c)* is the building in which the governing body of a state meets. It might help you to remember the difference between capit*a*l and capit*o*l if you note that most capitols are buildings with domes.

External refers to that which is outside, rather than inside. Its antonym, *internal,* refers to that which is inside rather than outside. The skin is the body's only *external* organ. The heart, lungs, liver, and kidneys are *internal* organs.

A related word to *external* is *exterior;* its antonym is *interior.* An *exterior* door is one on the outside; an *interior* door is one inside a building that connects one room with another.

Lesson 19

Word List
Study the definitions of the words below; then do the exercises for the lesson.

audition
    n. A short performance by an actor or musician as a test for a particular job.
[*Auditions* for the school band will be held tomorrow.]
    v. To try out for.
[Six people *auditioned* for the part of Helen Keller in the fourth grade play.]

create
    v. To bring into being; to produce for the first time.
[The computer industry has *created* many new jobs.]
    creative *adj.* Having new and original ideas.
[Mozart was one of the most *creative* musicians that ever lived.]
    creation *n.* The act of bringing into being; something created.
[The *creation* of three new teaching positions means that classrooms will be less crowded.]

elevate
    v. To lift up; to raise to a higher level.
[Jane Austen *elevated* the English novel to new heights.]
    elevation *n.* Height.
[I have to look up the *elevation* of Mt. Monadnock for my chart.]

eliminate
    v. To get rid of; to remove or leave out.
[Zeb decided to *eliminate* the last paragraph because his report was too long.]
    elimination *n.* A getting rid of.
[The *elimination* of the Red Sox from the pennant race upset my mother terribly.]

engage
    v. 1. To put to work; to hire.
[The Beachfront Restaurant *engages* extra help every summer.]
    2. To keep busy or active.
[Wen Lin tried to *engage* her cousin in conversation, but she was very shy.]
    3. To bind oneself to do something, especially to marry.
[My parents got *engaged* on New Year's Eve.]

entrance
    v. (en 'transs) To fill with joy or delight.
[The young dancers *entranced* the audience with their grace and beauty.]
    entrancing *adj.* delightful
[The songs were so *entrancing* that we hated to see the performance end.]

essential
    adj. Most important; very necessary.
[Fresh fruit and vegetables are *essential* to a good diet.]
    essentials *n. pl.* Something that cannot be done without.
[I packed my overnight bag with my toothbrush and other *essentials*.]

foremost
    adj. First in importance, time, or place.
[This new play by America's *foremost* playwright is breaking all box office records.]

forsake
    v. To have nothing more to do with; to turn one's back on.
[I'd never *forsake* my old friends if I became rich and famous.]

recognize   *v.* 1. To know and remember upon seeing.
[I *recognized* the name, but not the face.]
2. To admit the truth or accept the existence of.
[For many years, the U.S. was unwilling to *recognize* the government of China.]
3. To accept and approve.
[The manager told my mother that the company *recognizes* the good job she does.]

sentimental   *adj.* Expressing feelings of love, pity, etc. to excess.
[The movie was so *sentimental* everyone was in tears.]

source   *n.* The thing or place from which something comes.
[We decided to go on a trip to reach the *source* of the Nile River.]

tour   *n.* A trip or journey in which one usually returns to the starting point.
[The band played over twenty concerts on its *tour* of the Midwest.]
v. To travel to different places.
[My cousin Anna and I *toured* the old part of Montreal in a horse-drawn carriage.]

tradition   *n.* A belief, custom, or usual way of doing things, handed down within families or other groups.
[Fireworks on July 4 are an American *tradition*.]
traditional   *adj.* Handed down from age to age.
[My whole family enjoys getting together for a *traditional* Passover seder.]

trio   *n.* A group of three people.
[Luis plays the cello in a *trio*.]

19A Finding Meanings

Choose two phrases to form a sentence that correctly uses a word from Word List 19. Write each sentence in the space provided.

1. (a) the things that are proposed.
   (b) Traditions are
   (c) Essentials are
   (d) the things considered necessary.

   _____

2. (a) know or remember it.
   (b) To recognize a piece of work is to
   (c) To create a piece of work is to
   (d) make changes in it.

   _____

3. (a) passed down over time.
   (b) A traditional custom is one
   (c) that is no longer practiced.
   (d) A sentimental custom is one

   _____

4. (a) A creation is
   (b) A tour is
   (c) a small group.
   (d) something produced for the first time.

   _____

5. (a) to consider.   (c) to delight.
   (b) To entrance is   (d) To audition is

---

6. (a) turn one's back on that person.   (c) To engage someone is to
   (b) protect that person.   (d) To forsake someone is to

---

7. (a) Elimination of something is   (c) Elevation of something is
   (b) finding a new and different use for it.   (d) getting rid of it.

---

8. (a) To audition someone is to   (c) hire that person.
   (b) To engage someone is to   (d) get rid of that person.

---

9. (a) a journey around a place.   (c) A source is
   (b) the answer to a puzzle.   (d) A tour is

19B Just the Right Word

Improve each of the following sentences by crossing out the italicized phrase and replacing it with a word (or a form of the word) from Word List 19.

1. Stephen Hawking is one of the world's *greatest and most important* experts on black holes.

2. At my parents' anniversary party a *group of three singers* sang popular songs from the forties and fifties.

3. We were able to locate the *place that was the beginning* of the river by following it and hiking up to the mountains.

4. The Pied Piper's job was to *get rid of* the rats from the town of Hamelin.

5. My cousin Becca and Juan Morales, her friend from grade school, became *promised to each other in marriage* on June 1.

6. Because I am so short, I have to *put at a higher level* every piano stool I sit on.

7. I always cry at weddings because I'm so *easily affected by romantic feelings.*

8. Sequoya *brought into being for the first time* a written language for the Cherokee people.

9. The government *admits the existence of* the need for laws to protect the wetlands.

10. The *short performances that people gave who were trying out* for places in the orchestra lasted all day.

11. We returned again and again to Trinidad because it is such a(n) *delightful and pleasurable* island.

19C Applying Meanings

Circle the letter of each correct answer to the questions below. A question may have more than one correct answer.

1. Which of the following might one *audition* for?
   (a) a job with a band
   (b) an apartment rental
   (c) a part in a play
   (d) a factory position

2. Which of the following is *essential* for college?
   (a) graduation from high school
   (b) being on a sports team
   (c) a birth certificate
   (d) good grades

3. Which of the following are Halloween *traditions?*
   (a) trick or treating
   (b) bobbing for apples
   (c) carving a jack-o-lantern
   (d) making pumpkin pie

4. Which of the following might one *tour?*
   (a) an automobile
   (b) a museum
   (c) a cruise ship
   (d) a film studio

5. Which of the following might one *forsake?*
   (a) one's friends
   (b) one's family
   (c) one's career
   (d) one's health

6. Which of the following might *elevate* one's spirits?
   (a) being hailed by a friend
   (b) a pessimistic remark
   (c) being jeered by a crowd
   (d) finishing a lot of work

7. Which of the following might *entrance* a child?
   (a) a red balloon
   (b) a melancholy tale
   (c) a funny clown
   (d) a threatening gesture

8. Which should one *eliminate* for good health?
   (a) a balanced diet   (c) smoking cigarettes
   (b) regular check-ups   (d) exercise

19D Completing the Thought

Read each sentence below and fill in the blank with the correct word (or a form of the word) from the word list.

1. Tears came into Molly's eyes as she listened to the singer performing the Irish songs she had listened to as a child. The songs made her feel _____.

2. When Joe met Jean, he knew right away that he wanted to marry her. They soon became _____.

3. When Sophie entertains at children's parties, she wears baggy pants, enormous shoes, an orange wig, and a bright red nose. She likes the _____ clown costume.

4. The children sat spellbound in their seats at the ninth grade's performance of "Peter Pan." They were _____.

| audition |
| create |
| elevate |
| engage |
| entrance |
| foremost |
| recognize |
| sentimental |
| source |
| tradition |

5. Dylan looked everywhere for the store that sold the muffins his mother liked. Finally, he found the _____.

6. Ms. Hollingworth taught us to use our imaginations and utilize whatever materials were available to make our pictures and sculptures. She encouraged us to be _____.

7. As soon as Sally heard the man speak, she knew at once that this was her long-lost cousin Tim. She _____ his voice.

8. Visitors to Lhasa sometimes have difficulty breathing because the Tibetan city is in the Himalayas, where the air is thin. Its _____ is quite high.

9. Wherever Yo Yo Ma performs, his concerts are sold out. He is one of the world's _____ cellists.

10. Min was rehearsing for a part in the play for several hours every day. She wanted to do well at her _____.

19E Narrative

Read the narrative below; then complete the exercise that follows.

MARTHA GRAHAM— ARTIST AND TEACHER

Martha Graham was one of the **foremost** dancers of the twentieth century. She founded a dance company that performed modern dance for an ever-widening audience, and was **recognized** as one of modern dance's greatest teachers.

Before Martha Graham's time, dance as a serious art form meant French and Russian ballet, which had remained largely unchanged since the nineteenth century. It told stories that were often **sentimental** and far removed from the real world, and followed fixed patterns of movement. Female dancers wore **traditional** tight-waisted costumes with short skirts, tights, and stiffened ballet shoes that enabled them to dance on their toes. Music was usually classical, often written especially for the ballet.

Martha Graham began by **eliminating** from her dances everything that she felt was unnecessary. What remained was a new kind of dance, stripped to its **essentials** with bare stage settings and the simplest of costumes. Her dancers were usually barefoot and wore loose, flowing clothes. Her subjects were drawn from a great variety of **sources** that included Native American life, scenes from American history, and the poetry of Emily Dickinson. She tried to develop a kind of dance that expressed human feelings as well as told a story.

Martha Graham's lifelong interest in dance began in 1912 when, at the age of seventeen, she saw Ruth St. Denis perform in San Francisco as part of her American **tour**. St. Denis was heavily influenced by Japanese, Indian, and Spanish dances, and Graham was **entranced** by what she saw. She began taking dancing lessons, and when she was twenty-two she successfully **auditioned** for the Denishawn dance company, run by Ruth St. Denis and her husband, Ted Shawn. Graham stayed with the company for seven years and became one of its leading dancers.

In 1924, Martha Graham decided temporarily to **forsake** the life of a performer to concentrate on teaching and developing her own style of dancing. She returned to the New York stage two years later with a **trio** of female dancers formed from her best students; in 1930 she formed the much larger Martha Graham Dance Company. She preferred women dancers; not until 1938 did she **engage** male dancers to appear on stage with her. "Modern dance," she once said, "isn't anything in my mind except one thing—the freedom of women in America."

Her last public performance took place in 1969, when she was seventy-four years old. She had won over all her critics and had **elevated** modern dance to a new American art form. When she died in 1991, at the age of ninety-six, she was at work creating a new dance for her company. That unfinished work, *The Eyes of the Goddess*, was performed by her company shortly after her death as a tribute to one of America's greatest artists.

Answer each of the following questions in a sentence. If a question does not contain a vocabulary word, use a vocabulary word in your answer. Use each word only once. Questions and answers will then contain all fifteen words (or forms of the words) from this lesson's word list.

1. How do people around the country get to see dance companies?

   _____

2. How did Martha Graham change the style of dance?

   _____

3. What were **traditional** costumes like?

   _____

4. How would you describe the Martha Graham style of dance?

   _____

5. What were French and Russian ballet like?

   _____

6. Where did Martha Graham get ideas for her dances?

   _____

7. How did Martha Graham feel about Ruth St. Denis's performance?

   _____

8. Why did Martha Graham **forsake** performing in 1924?

   _____

9. What is the meaning of **engage** as it is used in the narrative?

   _____

10. How many other dancers did Martha Graham need to perform with her as a **trio**?

    _____

11. What is the meaning of **recognized** as it is used in the narrative?

_____

12. What was Martha Graham doing at the time of her death?

_____

13. What does the narrative say was Martha Graham's greatest achievement?

_____

14. Why is Martha Graham famous?

_____

15. What do you have to do to get into a dance company?

_____

WORDLY WISE

If you **audition** for a part in a play, you want to make sure that you are _heard_. The word itself suggests this; it comes from the Latin verb _audire,_ which means "to hear." Other words formed from this root include the following:

Audible, loud enough to be heard (an _audible_ whisper);

Audio, intended to be heard (an _audio_ tape);

Audience, a group of people gathered together to hear (and also to see) whatever is being performed for their enjoyment;

Auditorium, a large room in which people come together to hear a presentation;

Auditory, having to do with the ear (the _auditory_ nerve).

❖ ❖ ❖ ❖ ❖ ❖

A **trio** is a group of three, especially a group of three musicians or other entertainers. The word comes from the Latin (and Greek) word for "three." Other Latin numbers give us the following: _duet,_ two performers or a piece to be performed by two persons, from the Latin _duo; quartet,_ a group of four, from the Latin _quattuor; quintet,_ a group of five, from the Latin _quintus; sextet,_ a group of six, from the Latin _sex; septet,_ a group of seven, from the Latin _septem;_ and _octet,_ a group of eight, from the Latin _octo._

❖ ❖ ❖ ❖ ❖ ❖

Entrance has two pronunciations: en 'transs, and 'en transs. The more common pronunciation, 'en transs, means _a way to go inside someplace or something._ En 'transs, _to fill with joy or delight,_ which appears in this lesson, is less common.

Lesson 20

Word List

Study the definitions of the words below; then do the exercises for the lesson.

arrest
    v. 1. To stop the movement or progress of.
[The doctors were able to *arrest* the spread of the disease.]
2. To seize and charge with breaking the law.
[When the police *arrested* the suspect, they found the stolen jewelry in his pocket!]
n. The act of arresting.
[The police officer who made the *arrest* was the chief witness at the trial.]

capable
    adj. Able to do things well; skilled.
[She is so *capable* she remodeled her bathroom herself.]
capable of 1. Ready and able to.
[Even in his nineties, Bob Hope is still *capable of* entertaining an audience.]
2. Having the qualities necessary for.
[The stadium is *capable of* holding fifty thousand people.]

congratulate
    v. To express pleasure for a person's success or good fortune.
[Allow me to *congratulate* you on your victory.]
congratulations *n. pl.* Good wishes.
[Our class made Zel a card that said, "*Congratulations* on winning the 10k race!"

despise
    v. To scorn and dislike strongly; to consider unworthy of respect.
[The French nobles *despised* the peasants, whom they considered lacking in refinement.]

dispute
    n. A strong difference of opinion; an argument.
[The feuding neighbors were unable to settle their *dispute* and finally took it to court.]
v. To question the truth or value of.
[When her parents *disputed* the value of her new bike, Rona produced an article in *Cycling* that praised it.]

eventual
    adj. Coming at a later time; happening as a result of.
[Years of practice led to his *eventual* success as a Wimbledon tennis champion.]

helm
    n. 1. The wheel or tiller used to steer a boat.
[The skipper said I could take the *helm* since the sea was calm.]
2. A position of control.
[With a new president at the *helm*, there is a strong likelihood that the company will grow.]

humiliate
    v. To treat in a way that takes away a person's pride or self respect.
[His fellow workers *humiliated* Hans Christian Andersen because he seemed so strange.]
humiliation *n.* The act of humiliating or the state of being humiliated.
[The emperor in the story could not hide his *humiliation* at the way the two "tailors" had tricked him.]

implore	*v.* To plead with or beg for with much feeling.
	[I *implored* my parents to let me go with them.]
insert	*v.* To put in.
	["Please *insert* fifty-five cents," said the voice on the phone.]
	n. An extra piece sewn or put in place.
	[My new shirt has a lace *insert* at the neck.]
outrage	*n.* 1. Anger caused by injury or insult.
	[The decision to close the school caused *outrage* among the parents.]
	2. Anything that causes resentment or anger; a wicked or brutal act or remark.
	["Capital punishment is an *outrage* and should be banned!" she shouted.]
	v. To fill with anger or resentment.
	[The way some people allow their dogs to run without a leash *outrages* me.]
pierce	*v.* 1. To pass or break through.
	[A beam of light suddenly *pierced* the darkness.]
	2. To make a hole through.
	[The needle *pierced* the thick fabric easily.]
	piercing *adj.* Very loud and shrill.
	[The *piercing* cries of the seagulls woke me up.]
quiver	*v.* To shake with small, rapid movements; to tremble.
	[The child's lip *quivered* as if he were about to cry.]
	n. 1. A trembling.
	[There was a *quiver* in her voice as Mira told us about the accident.]
	2. A case for holding arrows.
	[Each archer was equipped with a bow and a *quiver* full of arrows.]
release	*v.* 1. To let go; to free.
	[The pigeons flew away as soon as I *released* them from their cages.]
	2. To make known.
	[A copy of the governor's speech was *released* to reporters at noon.]
	n. 1. A setting free.
	[Four years after his *release* from prison, Nelson Mandela was sworn in as South Africa's first black president.]
	2. A making known.
	[The publicity committee hurried to get out the press *release* so people would know about the play.]
sullen	*adj.* Silent from anger or hurt.
	[Tom grew from a *sullen* teenager into a friendly and outgoing young man.]

20A Finding Meanings

Choose two phrases to form a sentence that correctly uses a word from Word List 20. Write each sentence in the space provided.

1. (a) A quiver is
   (b) A release is
   (c) an extra piece put into place.
   (d) a case for arrows.

2. (a) A capable person is one who
   (b) whose self-respect has been lost.
   (c) An outraged person is one
   (d) is able to do things well.

3. (a) a rapid shaking movement.
   (b) An arrest is
   (c) A quiver is
   (d) a putting off until later.

4. (a) to deny that it is true.
   (b) To insert a story is
   (c) to make it known.
   (d) To release a story is

5. (a) An arrest is
   (b) A dispute is
   (c) a stopping by an officer of the law
   (d) a changing of one's mind.

6. (a) To humiliate someone is to
   (b) plead with that person.
   (c) make that person very angry.
   (d) To implore someone is to

7. (a) a sudden stop.
   (b) an argument.
   (c) A dispute is
   (d) A helm is

8. (a) is silently angry.
   (b) thinks fondly of the past.
   (c) A sullen person is one who
   (d) A humiliated person is one who

9. (a) to shock and anger that person.
   (b) to think highly of that person.
   (c) To despise someone is
   (d) To outrage someone is

10. (a) something that is removed.
    (b) An insert is
    (c) an extra piece put in place.
    (d) A helm is

20B Just the Right Word

Improve each of the following sentences by crossing out the italicized phrase and replacing it with a word (or a form of the word) from Word List 20.

1. Her high soprano voice suddenly *broke through* the silence of the auditorium.

2. They'll come around to your way of thinking *sooner or later*.

3. Jeff was almost in tears as he *begged and pleaded with* me to help him with his math homework.

4. Unlike her cheerful sister, Noa had a *dark and gloomy* nature.

5. Six quarters must be *put into the slot* before the washing machine will start.

6. I *questioned the correctness of* the price I was charged because the sign said "Everything Half-Price."

7. Mr. Singh gave the carpenters his *good wishes* on a remodeling job well done.

8. My *loss of pride in what I was doing* was so great when the audience didn't even applaud that I rushed off the stage.

9. Nan and Johanna took turns at the *wheel used to steer the boat* on their tour of the islands.

10. Annabel will do a good job building the new bathroom because she is so *skilled and able*.

11. I *have a strong dislike for* those who are cruel to animals.

20C Applying Meanings

Circle the letter of each correct answer to the questions below. A question may have more than one correct answer.

1. Which of the following might be *congratulated*?
   - (a) a winner
   - (b) a bride and groom
   - (c) a victim
   - (d) an intruder

2. Which of the following could be *released?*
   (a) a statement to the press   (c) a caged animal
   (b) a prisoner   (d) a door catch

3. Which of the following happens *eventually?*
   (a) you are born   (c) winter comes to an end
   (b) you die   (d) the football season begins

4. Which of the following has a *helm?*
   (a) a racing car   (c) a ship
   (b) a canoe   (d) a fortress

5. Which of the following might be *humiliating?*
   (a) being routed in a contest   (c) being hailed as a hero
   (b) demonstrating courage   (d) being jeered at

6. Which of the following would be an *outrage?*
   (a) jailing an innocent person   (c) banning free speech
   (b) discovering a cure for a disease (d) arresting a suspect

7. Which of the following can be *pierced?*
   (a) the skin   (c) the voice
   (b) the ears   (d) fog

8. Which of the following would we want *arrested?*
   (a) a lawbreaker   (c) the spread of a disease
   (b) the witness to a crime   (d) a pessimist

20D Completing the Thought

Read each sentence below and fill in the blank with the correct word (or a form of the word) from the word list.

1. Whenever I heard Mrs. Malamud's voice on the phone, I had to hold the receiver about six inches from my ear. Her voice was very _____.

2. After watching the caterpillar in the jar develop into a monarch butterfly, we took the jar out to the field and took off the lid. There we all watched its _____.

3. Dolly stopped halfway through the poem and seemed about to break down and weep. Her voice began to _____.

| capable |
| despise |
| dispute |
| helm |
| outrage |
| pierce |
| quiver |
| release |
| sullen |

4. The plane is equipped with the latest ramjets, making it possible for it to fly at incredible speeds. It is _____ of flying over 700 mph.

5. When the company ran into trouble, Jimmy Wu was brought in to run it, and in six months sales almost doubled. The stockholders were very glad he took the _____.

6. Gina got very little attention when she was little, and grew into an unhappy child. She was often quite _____.

7. When she found out he had not been telling her the truth about the accident, she told him he couldn't use her car again. She _____ lying.

8. My electric bill tripled this month, even though we weren't using any more electricity. I called the company to _____ the bill.

9. People in town were so angry at the cuts in the school budget that they held a rally at the capitol. Their _____ led them to organize.

20E Narrative

Read the narrative below; then complete the exercise that follows.

THE STORY OF WILLIAM TELL

In the town of Altdorf, Switzerland, stands a famous statue of William Tell, his son at his side, his crossbow slung over his shoulder. Although historians **dispute** William Tell's existence, and there is no evidence that he was a real person, Tell is a national hero to the Swiss people. He is a symbol of political and individual freedom.

Seven hundred years ago, the Swiss people were ruled by Austria. The governor of Switzerland was an Austrian named Gessler who **despised** the Swiss people and did not consider them **capable** of ruling themselves. One day, in order to **humiliate** them, he put his cap on a pole and ordered everyone in the town of Altdorf who passed by to bow before it. The Swiss people regarded the cap as a symbol of Austrian rule, and they detested it. However, the people of Altdorf had no choice, and they **sullenly** obeyed the order.

William Tell, a peasant from a nearby Swiss village, happened to be visiting Altdorf with his young son. Tell was famous for his skill as a boatman and was equally expert with the crossbow. He was also a proud man, and the people of the village watched as he approached the cap. Would he bow his head before it? No one was surprised to see him walk past the cap with his head held high. The Austrian guards **arrested** him for his "crime" and took him before the governor.

Gessler had heard of William Tell's remarkable skill with the crossbow, and it amused him to give his prisoner a choice: either go to prison or win freedom by shooting an apple from the top of his son's head at a hundred paces. Tell did not hesitate. After pacing out the distance, he removed two arrows from his **quiver.** He **inserted** the first one in the groove of his crossbow; the second arrow he tucked in his belt. He wound the spring of the crossbow and took careful aim. There was a tense silence as those watching waited for him to **release** the arrow. When he did so, it flashed through the air, splitting the apple cleanly in two. The boy was unharmed. After **congratulating** William Tell for demonstrating such skill, Gessler asked what the second arrow was for.

William Tell looked him in the eye and said, "If the first arrow had hurt my son, the second would have **pierced** your heart." Gessler was **outraged** by this reply and ordered Tell locked up for the rest of his life. But the boat that was carrying him across the lake to prison ran into a storm. The frightened crew knew that William Tell was a skilled boatman. They untied him and **implored** him to take over. Tell seized the **helm.** While the crew cowered below, he steered the boat toward the rocky shore. At the last moment he leaped ashore and escaped.

Once free, he lay in wait at a place where he knew Gessler would pass. When the governor did so, the arrow from William Tell's bow found its mark. Gessler died instantly. The news of William Tell's deed spread quickly and made him a hero to the Swiss people. It helped to unite them in their struggle and **eventually** led to their freedom from Austrian rule.

Answer each of the following questions in a sentence. If a question does not contain a vocabulary word, use a vocabulary word in your answer. Use each word only once. Questions and answers will then contain all fifteen words (or forms of the words) from this lesson's word list.

1. Do you think William Tell's **arrest** was unjust?

   _____

2. How did the people of Altdorf show their feelings when told to bow before the cap?

   _____

3. Why was it **humiliating** for the Swiss to bow before Gessler's cap?

   _____

4. What does it mean to say that historians **dispute** the existence of William Tell?

   _____

5. What were Gessler's feelings toward the Swiss people?

_____

6. Why did Gessler order William Tell to jail?

_____

7. Why did Gessler think that Austria had a right to rule the Swiss people?

_____

8. Why was everyone silent as they watched William Tell?

_____

9. What did William Tell do with the two arrows?

_____

10. What is the meaning of **quiver** as it is used in the narrative?

_____

11. What did William Tell intend to do with the second arrow?

_____

12. How did Gessler react when the arrow split the apple in two?

_____

13. Where was the crew while William Tell was at the **helm**?

_____

14. How can we tell that the crew could not handle the boat?

_____

15. Did Gessler's death have an immediate result?

_____

WORDLY WISE

To **humiliate** someone is to lower that person's reputation in the eyes of others. The word comes from the Latin *humilis,* which means "low." This Latin word in turn comes from an older Latin word, *humus,* which means "earth" or "dirt." To *humiliate* someone is to treat that person "like dirt." Incidentally, *humus* is the English word for the decayed vegetable matter that enriches soil.

Humble (Word List 14) comes from the same Latin root. Someone of *humble* birth occupies a *low* position in society. To *humble* oneself is to *lower* oneself in the eyes of others.

There is another noun formed from *humiliate,* in addition to *humiliation.* It is related in meaning, but with an important difference. *Humility* is the state of being humble. It is considered by many to be a desirable state, the opposite of being boastful or vain.

Humiliation suggests being disgraced, having one's pride taken away.

❖ ❖ ❖ ❖ ❖ ❖ ❖

If you weep while **imploring** a person to do something, your pleading might have a better chance of succeeding. At least, that is what the word suggests. It comes from the Latin *plorare,* which means "to cry out" or "to weep."

❖ ❖ ❖ ❖ ❖ ❖ ❖

A **sullen** person is likely to shun the company of others or to be shunned by them. In either event, such a person is likely to be left alone. This should come as no surprise since the word comes from the Latin *solus,* which means "alone." For a number of other words formed from this Latin root see Wordly Wise 13.

CROSSWORD PUZZLE

Solve the crossword puzzle below by studying the clues and filling in the answer boxes. Clues followed by a number are definitions of words in Lessons 17—20. The number gives the word list in which the answer to the clue appears.

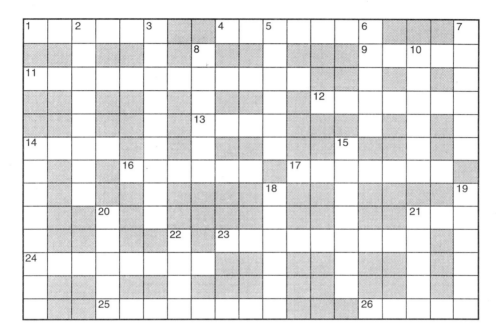

Clues Across

1. To go with, to guide or protect (17)
4. To think well of (17)
9. Opposite of *higher*
11. To express pleasure for a person's success (20)
12. To lift up; to make higher (19)
13. Of great size; enormous (18)
14. A long, bitter quarrel (18)
16. To make a hole through (20)
17. A person who makes a living from the soil (18)
21. You write with this
23. To take away the pride or self-respect of (20)
24. To fill with delight (19)
25. To warn someone that you might harm them (18)
26. Country in North Africa whose capital is Cairo

Clues Down

2. To end; to finish (17)
3. A custom handed down over time (19)
5. Used to make French fries
6. A person who is older (17)
7. To stop the movement or progress of (20)
8. A case for holding arrows (20)
10. Used to fight with
14. A building strong enough to be used for defense (18)
15. Something that gets in the way (18)
18. To send for (17)
19. An extra piece sewn or put in place (20)
20. To deserve (17)
21. Of little importance (18)
22. A tooth _____ or stomach _____